ENEMY AT BAY

At 0645 hours, lookouts aboard *Fanshaw Bay* heard antiaircraft fire to the north. The ack-ack puzzled the American sailor—why were their men firing? Only moments later, the radar screen signaled unidentified surface ship contacts. And almost at the same time, the radio picked up some heavy, garbled Japanese chatter. But surely there were no Japanese ships in the area . . . and then the report came in:

"Four Japanese battleships, eight cruisers, and a dozen destroyers; sailing directly south at 20 to 25 knots."

Captain Carsen couldn't believe it. "It's got to be a mistake. It can't be Japanese!"

"Enemy curisers and battleships! Cruisers and battleships! Bearing, 170 degrees!" The unmistakable pagoda masts of Japanese heavy warships were nearing.

Admirals Sprague, Johnson and Carsen looked at each other in amazement. "Son of a bitch!" they cried, as they suddenly realized they were the only American ship in the area . . .

A SPECTACULAR NEW ADULT WESTERN SERIES

SHELTER #1: PRISONER OF REVENGE　　　　(598, $1.95)
by Paul Ledd
After seven years in prison for a crime he didn't commit, ex-confederate soldier, Shelter Dorsett, was free and plotting his revenge on the "friends" who had used him in their scheme and left him the blame.

SHELTER #2: HANGING MOON　　　　(637, $1.95)
by Paul Ledd
In search of a double-crossing death battalion sergeant, Shelter heads across the Arizona territory—with lucious Drusilla, who is pure gold. So is the cargo hidden beneath the wagon's floorboards. And when Shell discovers it, the trip becomes a passage to hell.

SHELTER #3: CHAIN GANG KILL　　　　(658, $1.95)
by Paul Ledd
Shelter finds himself "wanted" by a member of the death battalion who double-crossed him seven years before *and* by a fiery wench. Bound by lust, Shelter aims to please; burning with vengeance, he seeks to kill!

SHELTER #4: CHINA DOLL　　　　(682, $1.95)
by Paul Ledd
The closer the *Drake* sails to San Francisco, the closer Shelter is to the target of his revenge. Shell thinks he's the only passenger on board, until he discovers the woman hiding below deck whose captivating powers steer him off course.

Available wherever paperbacks are sold, or order direct from the Publisher. Send cover price plus 50¢ per copy for mailing and handling to Zebra Books, 21 East 40th Street, New York, N.Y. 10016. DO NOT SEND CASH!

VALOR AT SAMAR

BY LAWRENCE CORTESI

ZEBRA BOOKS

KENSINGTON PUBLISHING CORP.

ZEBRA BOOKS

are published by

KENSINGTON PUBLISHING CORP.
21 East 40th Street
New York, N.Y. 10016

Copyright © **1980** by Lawrence Cortesi

Printed in the United States of America

The author would like to thank Mrs. Geneva McGlauflin, Inter Library Loan supervisor of the Troy, N. Y. Public Library for her efforts in finding rare personal account information for this book. I would also like to thank Mr. D. C. Allard of the Naval Historical Center's archives section for digging out numerous records on this naval engagement, especially the action reports of both the U. S. Taffy 3 and the Japanese 1st Striking Force.

L. J. Cortesi

Chapter One

By the midsummer of 1944, the Japanese understood a sobering truth. General Douglas MacArthur, commander in chief of the Allied Southwest Pacific Forces in World War II, now had the means to carry out a boast he had made in 1942. "I shall return" (to the Philippines). During the latter part of 1943 and throughout 1944, the Americans in the Pacific had successfully carried out a two prong drive toward the Japanese homelands. General MacArthur had completed the conquest of New Guinea, the Solomons, and Morotai, the last obstacle on the southern route to the Philippines. Admiral Chester Nimitz, commander in chief of Pacific Area Forces, had taken the Marshall Islands, the Carolines, Saipan, and the Palau Islands, Now, the Americans were ready to strike into the Philippines. The only question facing the Japanese: where and when would the Americans strike?

By mid-1944, the fully confident U. S. forces held a vast superiority in planes, men, and ships. The Japanese would need to muster whatever they could and use such forces in a most strategic manner if they hoped to stop any American invasion of the Philippines.

On October 20, 1944, MacArthur made good his boast to return to the Philippines when American troops landed on Leyte Island. One day after the invasion, MacArthur himself came ashore. Foreign correspondents reported his return and newspapers throughout the world carried the story on their front pages.

But, a few days after the invasion, General Douglas MacArthur and his 100,000 troops found themselves in danger of annihilation because American naval commanders had made a grave miscalculation. The miscue would allow a powerful Japanese naval fleet to sail unmolested toward the Leyte beachhead with the possibility that the Japanese would wipe out the Leyte landing sites. The Americans would need every ounce of courage and plenty of Yankee ingenuity to cope with this crisis, one of the worst of the Pacific war.

During four breathless hours, no one knew if courage and ingenuity would be enough.

The Japanese recognized a vital fact: the Philippine Islands group lay along the supply route between their rich East Indies raw material sources and their homeland war factories. Tankers brought oil to Japan while freighters brought metal ores and food to Japan. If the Americans cut off this supply line, the Japanese home islands might wither and die for lack of vital resources. While the Americans continually approached westward and northward, wresting one island after another from Nippon, the Japanese merely lamented these losses, for the defeats of the past year had not affected their life-line from the Indies. But, the fall of the Philippines would bring disastrous results.

The Japanese had expected the island strong-hold of Saipan to stop any American advance on the Philippines from the east, while the island of Morotai represented the final obstacle to any approach to the Philippines from the south. Prime Minister Hideki Tojo had promised his people, the military leaders, and his cabinet that Saipan and Morotai would never fall into American hands. But, in July of 1944, Saipan fell and in September of 1944 the Americans captured Morotai. The loss of these two strategic islands brought the fall of the Tojo cabinet. General Yoshigiro Umezu, Army chief of staff, took over the reins of government, while he still ran the Imperial Military Japanese Headquarters.

With his military staff in Tokyo, Umezu drew up the Sho-Go plan, "Operation Victory," for the defense of the Philippines. When he completed the plan, he called on General Tomoyuki Yamashita, the Tiger of Malaya, to assume command for the defense of the Philippines. Yamashita left his remote post in Manchuria to carry out these preparations—a hard challenge, considering the vast military resources of the United States by late summer of 1944.

"I am not certain that I nor anyone else can really hold the Philippines," Yamashita wrote in a private letter to his wife. "I have learned the Philippine people still support the Americans instead of accepting our co-prosperity efforts in the Far East. I will need to convince these people that their

9

true fortunes lie in cooperating with the Japanese empire."

When Yamashita surveyed the Philippine military posture, he found the Japanese 14th Army a unit in name only. The 14th only included four brigades and the 16th Infantry Division. He decided he needed at least fifteen more combat divisions to defend the Philippines, a request Japan could not fulfill. However, Imperial Headquarters did send Yamashita five more divisions—the 1st, 8th, 28th, 30th, and 102nd.

Yamashita then called on the Japanese puppet president of the Philippines, Lapuz Laural, in Manila. "You must work harder to convinced your people that it is in their best interest to cooperate with us."

"Too many do not listen," Laural replied. "They still support the Philippine guerillas."

"The Philippines will be reinforced with vast numbers of imperial troops, dozens of air units, and strong naval forces," Yamashita emphasized. "The Americans cannot succeed if they invade the Philippines. I will demand General MacArthur's surrender as I demanded and obtained the surrender of General Percival in Singapore. Your people should understand this, and they should understand the consequences if they fail to cooperate."

Quzzling President Laural promised to do what he could.

General Yamashita now planned vigorously to defend the Philippines. He had planned to fight a decisive battle on Luzon if the Americans invaded the Philippines. Through clandestine reports and

10

with the help of a Russian diplomat (Japan was not at war with Russia then), Yamashita learned that the probable target for an American invasion would be Leyte Island in the center of the island group, south of the major island of Luzon and north of the large island of Mindanao. The occupation of Leyte would give the Americans a centrally located position from which they could send their land based aircraft and naval units to strike any part of the Philippines.

With the almost certain knowledge that the Americans would move into the Philippines through Leyte, General Yamashita decided on his decisive battle at Leyte. He appointed Lt. General Susaku Suzuki to command the 35th Army in the area of Leyte against the expected invasion. The 35th, however, numbered no more than 50,000 men, and among these Suzuki found ready for combat only the battle hardened 16th Division and one brigade. The Leyte commander, who had fought alongside Yamashita in Malaysia early in the war, said he could not hold Leyte with such minimal forces. Yamashita asked Suzuki to simply delay the Americans, while Yamashita strengthened Luzon for a major battle against American ground forces.

Yamashita possessed 27 airfields in the Philippines, including the old Clark and Nichols Fields outside of Manila in Luzon. 12 of these were on Luzon, while the remainder were scattered on the islands of Cebu, Negros, Mindanao and Leyte, including one at Tacloban and another at Dulag on Leyte.

Vice Admiral Shigeru Fukudome commanded

the Japanese 2nd Air Fleet in the Western Pacific. He counted a total of 737 planes, including 233 fighter planes among his bases in the Philippines and in Formosa, north of the Philippines. Imperial Headquarters promised Yamashita and Fukudome an additional 688 aircraft to strengthen the 2nd Air Fleet.

One of the major units of the 2nd Air Fleet was the 6th Base Air Force at Clark Field under Admiral Takijiro Onishi that included 237 aircraft, among which were 83 fighter planes. Imperial Headquarters promised Onishi an additional 203 planes to strengthen his air force.

Obviously, the Japanese navy was vital for the defense of the Philippines. In September of 1944, after the fall of Morotai, Prime Minister Umezu called to his office Admiral Soemu Toyoda, commander of the Japanese Combined Fleets. "Can we hold the Philippines until the end of the year?" Umezu asked.

"It will be very difficult," Toyoda answered.

"If we hold the Philippines, if we can repulse an invasion, the Americans may look favorably on peace overtures," Umezu said.

Toyoda nodded.

"General Yamashita has begun preparations to defend the Philippines and I have confidence in him. I would like you, Honorable Toyoda, to prepare a naval strategy that will aid General Yamashita in this endeavor."

Admiral Soemu Toyoda nodded and promised to come up with a naval plan to augment General Yamashita's ground defense for the Philippines.

Toyoda and his staff drew up a strategy called Sho-I, the naval plan for the Sho-Go blueprint to defend the Philippines. Toyoda's formula was rather simple, but daring, considering the superiority of the American navy. He knew the Americans had two powerful fleets in the Western Pacific. One included a fast carrier group with more than a dozen carriers and hundreds of planes under Admiral William "Bull" Halsey. The other fleet under Admiral Thomas Kinkaid included several battleships, many cruisers, countless destroyers, and small escort carriers. Kinkaid's fleet would most likely escort an American invasion to Leyte.

Toyoda's Sho-I strategy called for the use of three Japanese fleets. A northern force under Admiral Jisaburo Ozawa, a mobile carrier fleet, would include six aircraft carriers. A center force, the 1st Striking Force under Admiral Takeo Kurita, would include five battleships, eleven cruisers, and fifteen destroyers. A southern force, the 2nd Striking Force under Admiral Shoji Nishimura, included two tandem small fleets totalling two battleships, several cruisers, and about a dozen destroyers.

Toyoda knew that the Americans had a glaring weakness — an obsession to chase down and sink aircraft carriers. So, in his Sho-I plan, his mobile carrier fleet under Ozawa would decoy Admiral Halsey's powerful fast carrier fleet away from the Leyte battle areas, while his other fleets along with land based Japanese aircraft in the Philippines would deal with the U. S. transport vessels, supply ships, and U. S. ground troops who attempted to invade Leyte. Ozawa would merely feint with his mobile fleet to keep the American carrier fleet chasing him throughout the vast waters between Luzon and Formosa. Meanwhile, the 2nd Striking Force under Admiral Nishimura would sail through Surigao Strait to approach Leyte from the south.

The center force, 1st Striking Force under Admiral Takeo Kurita, would sail through San Bernadino Strait to approach the Leyte invasion site from the north. Kurita's powerful surface fleet and Nishimura's smaller tandem fleets would then complete a pincer movement into Leyte Gulf to destroy the invasion site. Hopefully, since Ozawa's carrier force lured away the American fast carrier fleet, U. S. carrier planes could not threaten the two surface fleets assigned to pulverize the Leyte landing sites.

Toyoda's strategy was a daring plan, but a good plan. If the Japanese succeeded, MacArthur would indeed be sorry he had ever attempted to recapture the Philippines.

The Americans, in the meantime, were flushed with success by October of 1944. Since the New Guinea and Solomon Islands campaigns in late 1942, the U. S. Navy, the air groups, and the ground forces had only known one victory after another. Some of these offensives in the Pacific had gone hard, with severe losses, such as the Saipan and Peleliu fights. However, the Americans had ultimately won. After the fall of Saipan and Morotai in July and September of 1944, the Americans did indeed prepare for an invasion of the Philippines. The counted on friendly Filipinos and Philippine guerillas to help out, a populace that had waited eagerly for 2½ years to drive the Japanese from their home islands.

The Americans never doubted their ability to succeed with a Philippine invasion, but U. S. commanders held varying opinions on how, when, and where to invade. Since the beginning of the Pacific war, the two Pacific commanders, General Douglas MacArthur, Commander in Chief of the Southwest Pacific Forces, and Admiral Chester Nimitz, Commander in Chief of the Pacific Area Forces, had rarely agreed on anything. Once again, MacArthur and Nimitz squabbled – this time on Operation King II, the plan to invade the Philippines. The Joint Chiefs of Staff in Washington finally forced a compromise on the two Pacific commanders, a plan that both MacArthur and Nimitz must follow.

For Operation King II, General MacArthur would command the invasion forces that included troops of the U. S. 7th, 24th, 32nd, 77th, and 96th Army Infantry Divisions, along with the 1st Cavalry Division. The 1st and 24th would land at Tacloban while the 7th and 96th Divisions would land to the south at Dulag. The 32nd and 77th would be in reserve. The first objective would be the seizure of the Tacloban and Dulag airfields.

The U. S. 7th Fleet under Admiral Thomas Kinkaid would support the landings with his 8 battleships, 8 cruisers, 22 destroyers, half dozen destroyer escorts, and submarine fleet. The 7th Fleet also included three small CVE aircraft carrier fleets that carried 20 to 30 aircraft each. The baby flat tops would carry out CAP over the invasion site, support ground forces, and conduct antisubmarine patrols.

15

The 3rd Fleet, Admiral William Bull Halsey's fast carrier fleet, would have the job of thwarting any Japanese attempt to stop the Philippine invasion. The powerful 3rd Fleet would remain on station near Leyte to intercept any Japanese air or naval units that tried to interfere with the amphibious landings. The 3rd Fleet would also deal with any Japanese attempt to bring reinforcement convoys into Leyte. Halsey's fleet included eleven aircraft carriers with hundreds of planes, both fighters and bombers. The fleet also included several cruisers, some 20 destroyers, and 4 battleships: USS New Jersey, USS Iowa, USS Alabama, and USS Massachusetts. The 3rd was no doubt the most powerful naval striking force ever assembled during World War II. Halsey kept his flag aboard USS New Jersey.

Besides its duties in the Philippines itself, the 3rd Fleet would also make carrier air strikes on Okinawa, Formosa, Luzon, and northern Leyte during the week beginning October 13 to destroy Japanese airfields and aircraft that might be used against the Leyte invasions. The major segment of the 3rd Fleet, TG 38, would also strike Bicol, Cebu, and Negros, destroying any Japanese planes there.

Both Admiral Soemu Toyoda and Admiral Jisaburo Ozawa had no illusions about Bull Halsey's 3rd Fleet and its powerful striking ability from both aircraft and surface ships. The Japanese admirals knew that the 3rd Fleet alone could stop any Japanese attempt to stop an invasion of the Philippines. Thus, the vital key in the Sho-I plan was to successfully lure the 3rd Fleet away from Leyte. Admiral Ozawa himself fully expected to lose his entire mobile carrier fleet in his decoy strategy against the 3rd Fleet. Still, he told Admiral Toyoda:

"If my death and the death of the courageous sailors under my command can save the Philippines, I will consider these deaths an honor."

Among the Americans, not everyone agreed with the plans for Operation King II. General George C. Kenney, commander of the American Far East Air Forces, did not believe that naval air power alone could stop the Japanese land based planes in the Philippines.

"Our intelligence tells us the Japanese have substantial air units on their many air bases in the Philippines, a full naval air fleet and army air units. Most of these enemy air units are within easy range of Leyte. We need heavy land based planes to knock out these bases. Those carrier planes don't have the punch of land based medium and heavy bombers."

Kenney's nearest land base to the Philippines, Morotai, lay several hundred miles from Leyte, and the FEAF commander saw no way to use his medium or heavy bombers to neutralize the Japanese bases at Luzon, especially the big airfields at Clark and Nichols, outside of Manila. Nor could Kenney believe that heavy and medium bombers of the 7th Air Force from their bases in the Palau Islands could do the job because these land based planes were also too far from Leyte.

Kenney was convinced that the Americans should first invade the Talaud Island Group south of Mindanao and then take Sarangani Bay on the south coast of Mindanao to establish a land based airfield. Heavy army aircraft from such a field could then be within range to support a Leyte invasion.

However, Admiral William Bull Halsey scoffed at Kenney's suggestions. "The Japanese Air Force in the Philippines is nothing but a hollow shell, operating on a shoestring," the 3rd Fleet commander said. "They can't make any kind of air assault that our carrier planes can't handle."

Then, strangely, Kenney's own subordinate, General Ennis Whitehead of the 5th Army Air Force, agreed with Halsey. "The Japanese have lost most of their competent pilots and maintenance men during the past two years in their defeats at Wewak, Manos, Kavieng, and Rabaul. I think the Japanese Air Force is finished. Navy air can take care of the preliminary job of supporting the Philippine invasion until we get airdromes on Leyte for land based aircraft."

Still, Kenney was not convinced. "If the Japanese intend to fight and they get some decent air support for their ground troops, I think, we'll be in for a lot of trouble."

"It's worth the gamble to have airbases centrally located in the Philippines," General Whitehead told Kenney.

Soon enough, Admiral Bull Halsey proved the ability of carrier based planes. During the week beginning October 13, several days before the Leyte invasion, Halsey's TG 38 carrier planes fought a knock down, drag out series of air battles with Japanese land based planes from the 2nd Air Fleet bases on Formosa. Nearly a thousand Japanese planes flew sorties against the 3rd Fleet, who responded

18

with almost 1,000 planes of their own. But, the Japanese air units failed to sink or seriously damage a single one of Halsey's carriers, although the Americans lost 78 planes. In return, however, the American carrier planes destroyed over 500 Japanese planes in the air and on the ground, almost half of Admiral Shigeru Fukudome's complement of 2nd Air Fleet aircraft on Formosa. Further, the carrier planes put more than a dozen Formosa air bases out of business.

The air victory by the 3rd Fleet killed any further criticism by General Kenney, for the victory proved for the first time that carrier planes could successfully deal with land based aircraft. Of course, not all things were equal. The 3rd Fleet possessed as many aircraft as did the Japanese. The 3rd also possessed experienced pilots to fight against the now green, ill trained Japanese pilots. Further, the Americal Hellcat and Corsair fighter planes were quite superior to the Japanese Oscar and Zero fighter planes.

After the Formosa air battles, Kenney launched a series of air strikes with medium and heavy land based bombers against the Japanese airfields in the southern islands of the Philippines, including Mindanao, while Halsey launched a series of carrier plane attacks against Japanese air bases on the northern islands of the Philippines, including Luzon. The American air strikes destroyed most of these fields along with countless Japanese fighters and bombers on the ground. Thus, the Japanese would respond to the American invasion of Leyte with only minimal air strikes.

In the early hours of October 20, 1944, U. S. naval guns and naval aircraft pounded the Leyte invasion sites for several hours. Then, waves of American troops went ashore. The U. S. infantrymen quickly established beachheads against light opposition, and the troops hastily solidified their beaches before moving inland to wrest all of Leyte from the Japanese.

Because of the heavy American air strikes throughout the Philippine Islands, strikes by both 5th Army Air Force out of Morotai and U. S. 3rd Fleet, Admiral Shigeru Fukudome of the 2nd Air Fleet could only send a few small formations to Leyte from their airfields in Luzon. Also, Fukudome was disinclined to send more, for Fukudome remembered too well the recent Formosa air battles against the American 3rd Carrier Fleet that had wreaked disaster on his 2nd Air Fleet. Fukudome feared that hundreds of U. S. carrier planes might again pounce on his aircraft formations over the Leyte invasion site. Besides, the 2nd Air Fleet commander had yet to receive the promised reinforcements in planes and pilots.

Still, the several formations of Japanese planes that did fly to Leyte had some measure of success. They thoroughly observed American activities at the landing sites and the Japanese aircraft did manage to sink the American transport Sonoma and damage several other vessels in Leyte Gulf.

In turn, the carrier planes from the small CVE carriers of 7th Fleet concentrated on supporting American ground troops that moved inland against Japanese ground troops. Meanwhile, carrier planes from Halsey's powerful 3rd Fleet continued to attack Japanese airfields at Cebu, Negros, Panay, and Luzon. Halsey concentrated on the destruction of grounded planes rather than runways.

"Our idea was to get enemy planes at the source," Halsey said later, "to destroy them before they could take off. We saw no reason to waste time and bombs on runways because the Japanese were too adept at filling holes."

During October 21-23, making some 850 sorties, the planes of the U. S. 3rd Fleet destroyed some 125 Japanese planes on the ground and in the air.

As soon as the Americans invaded Leyte, Imperial Headquarters in Tokyo decided to make an all out effort in Leyte. General Yoshigiro Umezu personally sent a message to General Susaku Suzuki of the 35th Army in Leyte:

"Take heart; resist our enemy fiercely for we will not abandon you. You may expect massive air support from the 2nd Air Fleet on 24 October, and you can expect a decisive sea battle on 25 October. You may also expect our navy to deliver to Leyte by 26 October heavy reinforcements of combat troops."

As added encouragement, General Tomoyuki Yamashita also sent a message to General Suzuki. "We are determined to take the offensive and to clean up the American invasion forces on Leyte."

Both the Dulag and Tacloban airfields had fallen into American hands by October 21, only 36 hours after the landings. Army engineers, with the help of Philippine laborers quickly set about to repair and improve the airstrips. By the 22nd, the advanced

21

echelons of the 5th U. S. Army Air Force's 49th and 475th Fighter Groups, along with an advanced echelon of the 1st Marine Air Wing, had arrived in Leyte. Meanwhile the 305th American Airdome Engineer Battalion had already begun laying a new airstrip on the Calaison Peninsula at Tacloban. The engineers had been asked to speed up construction because General George Kenney wanted his land based planes on Leyte as soon as possible.

On October 24, the Japanese indeed committed heavy aircraft formations over Leyte. An estimated 150 to 200 Japanese planes had sortied over Leyte Gulf. But, thanks to the U. S. carrier plane interceptions, very few of the Japanese planes made successful strikes on the Leyte beachheads. The Japanese air strikes had only temporarily halted airfield construction on Tacloban and at Dulag.

Still, aircraft construction was delayed because Seabees were unloading mounds of supplies at Calaison Point at the extreme tip of the narrow peninsula that was needed for the far end of the Tacloban airstrip. The stacks of supplies had hampered the work of the 305th Airdrome Engineers and Major Richard Davidson, the 305th commander, complained to General Kenney. The Far East Air Force commander had arrived at Leyte on October 23. When Davidson complained, General Kenney angrily called Admiral Thomas Kinkaid, the 7th Fleet commander.

"Admiral," the FEAF commander barked, "if those LST's keep unloading stuff on Calaison Point and clogging the area, I'll bulldoze those goddamn dumps right into the sea. We've got an airfield to complete."

"We've got to stack those supplies somewhere," Kinkaid said.

"Well stack them somewhere else," Kenney grumbled.

"All right, I'll see what I can do," Kinkaid answered.

The 7th Fleet commander was equally piqued. He had his own problems. More than 100,000 U. S. troops had now disembarked at Leyte. If they did not get their supplies of food, ammo, and other needs, General Douglas MacArthur would be complaining bitterly. Further, Admiral Thomas Kinkaid saw no need for a quick completion of the land based airfield. The hundreds of carrier planes from the powerful 3rd Fleet and Kinkaid's own CVE carriers had easily dealt with Japanese resistance.

Still, Kinkaid moved the supplies off the point and Richardson's aviation engineers then made rapid progress on the Tacloban airstrip. Kenney was satisfied. Within a week, the field would be ready for his 5th Air Force fighter planes and even light bombers.

Admiral Kinkaid grumbled irritably because Kenney had gotten his way. The 7th Fleet commander could not guess that within two days, the Tacloban airstrip would play a vital role in saving a large segment of his 7th Fleet, and perhaps in saving the Leyte invasion sites themselves.

Chapter Two

Vice Admiral Takeo Kurita, a stern faced, balding man, was perhaps the most reliable and dedicated of all Japanese naval commanders. Whatever his mission, and whatever the fortunes of battle, victory or defeat, Admiral Kurita never expressed joy or sorrow, elation or disappointment, excitement or moodiness. But one thing was certain, Kurita was a good servant of the emperor who simply took life as it came in a taciturn, but distinguished carriage. He would go anywhere to fight, regardless of odds, and this willingness to put his life on the line at any time had won him the highest respect from sailors under his command.

Kurita had been at war since the 1930's as an officer aboard a cruiser that bombarded Chinese ports. He had been an admiral since 1938, leading Japanese naval ships into battles in China, in the Manchurian skirmishes with the Russians in 1939, and then in World War II. He had commanded a cruiser attack force during the Battle of Midway, but superiors had recalled his fleet when he had come within 80 miles of Midway because the Japanese had lost the battle. In the process of retiring from Midway Island, Kurita had lost one of his cruisers.

However, Kurita had gained revenge in October of 1942 when his attack column of two battleships, several cruisers, and several destroyers had leveled Henderson Field on the night of October 17 during the Solomons campaign. Not only had Kurita whacked the field, but his efforts had enabled Japanese transport ships to successfully land ground troop reinforcements on Guadalcanal without American air resistance from Henderson Field.

Kurita's next major engagement had come during the battle for Saipan where he had been part of Admiral Ozawa's fleet. The Japanese had failed to stop the American conquest of this vital Japanese stronghold and Kurita had retired in disappointment. Now, the sober faced admiral prepared for still another Pacific engagement against the Americans.

In October of 1944, Admiral Takeo Kurita was 55 years old. By then, after serving in a long series of combat campaigns, he had become one of the most thoroughly experienced and capable commanders in the Japanese navy.

Ten days before the American invasion of Leyte, on October 10, 1944, Admiral Soemu Toyoda had met with Kurita, Admiral Jisaburo Ozawa, Admiral Shoji Nishimura, and Admiral Kiyohide Shima. As Toyoda outlined the Sho-I plan for the navy's duties in the defense of the Philippines, Kurita had never changed the sober expression on his face.

After the briefing, Kurita flew directly back to Singapore, where his 1st Striking Force lay at anchor in Lingga Roads off the Malaysian Peninsula.

25

Here, he readied his huge fleet to carry out whatever mission he must. His 1st Striking Force included five battleships, among them Yamato and Musashi with their new 18.5" guns, and the battleships Kongo, Hurana, and Nagata. The fleet also included ten heavy cruisers: Takao, Chokai, Maya, Myoko, Haguro, Atago, Kumano, Suzuya, Chikuma, and Tone. Finally, two light cruisers, Yahagi and Noshiro, led two destroyer divisions that totalled a dozen destroyers. When Kurita told his staff to prepare for a sail southward, the sailors expressed surprise, and even irritation.

Admiral Tomiji Koyanagi, Kurita's chief of staff, was astonished at the order to aweigh the fleet.

"Honorable Kurita," Koyanagi told his superior, "did you not tell Admiral Toyoda that what he proposed to do is impossible? How can we swiftly sail when we have no idea when or where the Americans will attempt an invasion of the Philippines? In fact, we are not even certain the Americans will make such an invasion."

· Koyanagi had every confidence in the 1st Striking Force's ability to beat back any American attempt to invade the Philippines. However, he frowned on the idea of sailing out with no clear cut goal.

"We must do as we are told," Kurita answered his chief of staff. "Admiral Toyoda has no doubt that the Americans will invade the Philippines by the end of this month and we must be prepared to destroy such an invasion fleet. We shall sail to Brunei Bay as ordered and there await further instructions."

Admiral Koyanagi obeyed in grim silence. He may have believed the order foolish without a definite time or place for attack, but Koyanagi too understood that orders must be carried out.

Conversely, Admiral Matome Ugaki, commander of the 1st Striking Force's battleship division, expressed delight with the Sho-I plan. He called together his commanders and thoroughly briefed them. He also asked his subordinates to have every combat man ready and every ship in fighting shape.

Admiral Matome Ugaki had been Admiral Yamomoto's chief of staff until that day in 1943 when American P-38 pilots ambushed Yamomoto's plane in the Solomons, shooting him down and killing him. Thus, Ugaki was anxious to extract revenge against the Americans.

On October 17, 1944, Ugaki and Koyanagi met with Kurita and other staff members for the final instructions. By now, Koyanagi had calmed down, while an eagerness swirled inside of Admiral Matome Ugaki. When Ugaki returned to the battleship Yamato, he found that his seamen had caught a hawk that had alighted on one of the battleship's main batteries.

"A good omen," Ugaki told his sailors. "We will place this hawk in a cage and keep it on the bridge, for such a species augurs a phrophecy of victory."

"Yes, Honorable Ugaki," a subordinate answered.

At 0100 hours, the wee hours of October 18, the huge 1st Striking Force sortied out of Lingga Roads and headed south for Brunei Bay in northern Borneo. The weather had cleared and the sea had settled to a relative calm. So, the fleet made good time and Kurita arrived in Brunei Bay in the wee hours of October 20, shortly before the Leyte invasion. Here he would refuel his ships and wait. He expected to leave Borneo within the week to arrive off Samar Island, northeast of Leyte, in time to strike the American invasion convoy that was expected to approach Leyte about the end of October.

However, only a few hours later, the Americans made their Leyte landings, much earlier than anticipated and caught the Japanese off guard. Kurita had yet to complete final preparations, and he could not leave Brunei Bay for two more days. The other fleets of the Sho-I plan were also making final preparations. So, Admiral Soemu Toyoda, commander in chief of the Japanese Combined Fleets, set the early morning of October 25 for the destruction of the American invasion sites at Leyte. Kurita's 1st Striking Force and Nishimura's 2nd Striking Force would meet off Leyte Gulf early on this October 25 morning.

At 0800 hours, October 22, the 1st Striking Force left Brunei Bay to keep its appointment with the other Sho-I fleet for the destruction of the American invasion site at Leyte. The 1st Striking Force sailed eastward, with both Kurita and Koyanagi now feeling more enthusiasm, since they now knew the time and place of their attack. Kurita, as he sat in the bridge of the fleet flagship, cruiser Atago, showed no emotion on his sober face. Koyanagi, however, moved about with eager anticipation. By October 23, this huge Japanese central force had cleared Palawan Passage between the Palawan Islands and Mindoro Island and began its sail towards San Bernadino Strait north of Samar Island.

Meanwhile, the southern Japanese force, the 2nd Striking Force under Admiral Nishimura had sortied from eastern Borneo. By the same October 23, both

28

Nishimura's van section and Admiral Kiyohide Shima's rear section of this southern force was sailing across the lower end of the Sulu Sea and heading for Surigao Strait between the islands of Bohol and Mindanao.

Far to the north, the northern force, Ozawa's mobile carrier fleet, had left the Inland Sea on October 20 and had simply moved southward in the Western Pacific southeast of Formosa and northeast of Luzon, the Philippines, most northerly island. Ozawa would merely wait for search planes from the powerful U. S. 3rd Fleet to find his mobile fleet and give chase.

But now, the first unexpected flaw emerged in the Sho-I plan. None of Halsey's 3rd Fleet planes could find Ozawa's carrier fleet, so both the U. S. fast carrier fleet and the U. S. 7th Fleet were loitering around Leyte Gulf on October 23, only 36 hours before the scheduled Japanese surface ship bombardment of Leyte, scheduled for 0600 hours, October 25.

On the late afternoon of 23 October, a pair of U. S. submarines discovered Kurita's 1st Striking Force south of Mindoro Island. The sub commanders of USS Darter and the USS Dace radioed the position and bearing of the Japanese fleet to Admiral Kinkaid, the 7th Fleet commander. Kinkaid immediately guessed that Kirita's powerful surface fleet would attempt a run through San Bernadino Strait, sail south along the east coast of Samar, and then steam into Leyte Gulf for a battleship-cruiser bombardment that would be reminiscent of the old days in 1942 during the Solomons campaign. In these circumstances, however, the Japanese would have a much bigger plum than old Henderson Field on Guadalcanal. Nearly 200 auxiliary vessels of all types were in Leyte Gulf, countless tons of supplies were stacked on the beaches, the 305th Aviation Engineers had a mass of equipment at the Dulag and Tacloban airfield construction sites, and over 100,000 American troops had been put ashore. In fact, the plum at Leyte might have even surpassed the healthy targets at Pearl Harbor.

When darkness arrived on the evening of October 23, the USS Darter sent several torpedoes into Kurita's fleet and successfully hit and sank Kurita's flag, the cruiser Atago. The second U. S. submarine, USS Dace, sent a string of torpedoes into a second cruiser, Maya, and sank this second ship. Finally, Darter and Dace sent torpedoes into the cruiser Takao, damaging her so badly that the cruiser was forced to return to Brunei Bay under escort of two destroyers. Consternation reigned among the commanders and sailors of the Japanese fleet. Admirals Kurita, Koyanagi, and other survivors of Atago floundered in the sea until a destroyer rescued them and took them aboard battleship Yamato, where Kurita transferred his flag. Other destroyers rescued survivors from Maya on this dark night.

When Japanese destroyers finally went after the American submarines, Darter and Dace went deep and successfully eluded their pursuers.

By the morning of October 24, Kurita had reassembled his fleet, now minus three cruisers, and he continued on towards San Bernadino Strait. He increased speed to clear the strait and reach his rendezvous at Leyte Gulf with the 2nd Striking

Force. But, at 0812 hours, October 24, a reconn plane from the 3rd Fleet carrier USS Intrepid sighted the 1st Striking Force east of Mindoro Island as the fleet headed for San Bernadino Strait.

"Holy Christ," the reconn pilot radioed Intrepid. "I never saw such a fleet: at least four or five battleships, a bunch of cruisers and I don't know how many destroyers."

"Where are they?"

"Just east of Mindoro and due north of Panay Island."

"Okay," the plotter aboard carrier Intrepid answered. The 3rd Fleet operator then called Admiral Halsey aboard flag New Jersey. Halsey, in turn, ordered immediate air strikes on this Japanese central force.

At about 0800 hours, the bulk of the American 3rd Fleet was lying about 260 miles northeast of Samar Island. Some of the TG 38 units, in fact, were even sailing eastward to the island of Ulithi to refuel and resupply after the Formosa air battles. Halsey recalled them at once while he ordered the rest of 3rd Fleet southwestward to close range on the discovered fleet, the 1st Striking Force.

Not until early afternoon had 3rd Fleet carriers come near enough to launch planes against Kurita's fleet. But when the strikes came, swarms of American aircraft were involved. Planes from carriers Intrepid, Cabot, Essex and Lexington conducted continual air assaults for most of the afternoon, as wave after wave of navy aircraft struck Kurita's ships. Before the 3rd Fleet air strikes ended, the powerful U. S. carrier fleet had conducted 257 sorties against 1st Striking Force.

Kurita frantically called Manila. "Where is the air cover? We are being attacked hourly by American aircraft. Where is the promised air cover to protect us?"

"I do not know, Honorable Kurita," somebody answered from the 2nd Air Fleet headquarters in Manila.

"Where is Admiral Fukudome?"

"I will get him."

Fukudome listened with dismay as Kurita laced into him. "Are we to ward off these endless formations of enemy aircraft with mere anti-aircraft guns? Where are the Zero fighter planes that were promised to protect us?"

"At once, Admiral, at once," Fukudome answered. "I will send out air units at once to forestall further enemy air attacks on your fleet."

Fortunately for Kurita, his anti-aircraft gunners were good and his helmsmen were adept. Japanese gunners shot down 18 American planes and effectively spoiled the aim of many aircraft attacks. The American Dauntless dive bombers and Avenger torpedo bombers had only scored major hits on two ships, battleship Musashi and cruiser Myoko. By 1430 hours, the American planes had battered the big battleship and she listed badly to port with uncontrolled flooding. She sank at dusk. Cruiser Myoko had been hit so badly she was forced to retire to Brunei Bay in Borneo.

Still, by 0640 hours, Kurita had had enough of the American air strikes. He reversed course and sailed west to avoid further punishment from the

U. S. carrier planes. When the last flight of American planes left the area at 0655 hours, the flight leader grinned. "That enemy fleet is finished," he radioed Halsey over his TBS. "We sank or damaged every ship in that fleet. Whatever's left is scooting west out of range. Nothing'll be coming through San Bernadino Strait, Admiral."

"Are you certain?" Halsey asked.

"Positive," the navy squadron commander answered. "Check with anybody you like and they'll tell you the same thing. That enemy fleet is finished."

Halsey did check with other carrier squadron leaders and he got the same reports: the enemy fleet had been totally macerated by the afternoon air attacks and the remnants were now speeding westward. They would not likely come back.

"Okay," Halsey answered. "I'll ask Admiral Kinkaid to send a unit from his 7th Fleet to finish off any cripples they can find."

A battleship! Sink a battleship and naval pilots become blinded to all else. The awesome sight of Musashi going down was enough to convince the carrier pilots of the 3rd Fleet that they had all but destroyed the Japanese navy. Further, Admiral William Bull Halsey, a totally air minded admiral, had no doubts that carrier planes could sink the largest surface fleet afloat. So, he believed the exaggerated claims of his carrier pilots.

Kurita took stock as he sailed westward and learned to his surprise that none of his other vessels, including his other four battleships, had suffered more than minor damage, nothing that would impair their fighting ability. He then felt ashamed for making this retreat. With obvious guilt, he called Admiral Toyoda to report his decision. "We have been under repeated attacks by American carrier aircraft and I considered it advisable to retire temporarily from the zone of enemy air attacks."

"What were your losses?" Toyoda asked.

"Since leaving Brunei Bay, we have lost the battleship Musashi and the cruisers Atago and Maya. Both the cruisers Takeo and Myoko were so badly damaged that they were forced to return to Borneo."

"And what of your other vessels?"

"They have suffered only minor damage."

"I have word that Nishimura's 2nd Striking Force is on course. He will clear the Surigao Strait this evening and he should arrive at Leyte Gulf on schedule. Is it possible, Admiral Kurita, that you can reverse course and continue towards San Bernadino Strait? I have been assured by Admiral Fukudome that Mitsubishi fighter aircraft are on the way to give you air cover."

"I have been grieved by this reversal of course. But, if I am to resume the sail to keep the schedule at Leyte Gulf, I will need to increase speed to 22 knots."

"I beg you to do so," Admiral Toyoda said.

Kurita pondered a course of action for the next few moments. But then, at 1714 hours, Zeroes from the 761st Air Group emerged over Kurita's fleet. The group leader, Captain Shoichi Sugita, called the fleet admiral. "We will maintain cover as long as you need us, Honorable Kurita."

The arrival of the Japanese planes prompted Admiral Takeo Kurita to act. At 1730 hours, he reversed course and once more sailed towards San Bernadino Strait. This time he moved at 22 knots so he could make his rendezvous on time with the 2nd Striking Force.

"We have been harassed, Tomiji," Kurita said to his chief of staff, "but we are not yet beaten."

"True," Admiral Koyanagi answered. "But, if the Gods favor us, we will complete this important mission." Koyanagi looked at the calm sea and then at the planes overhead. He then stared at Admiral Kurita, looking sympathetically at the 1st Striking Force commander. "All is quiet now Takeo. You have suffered much these past two days and you have had no sleep. I urge you to return to your quarters and rest. Should anything of importance occur, I will call you."

"I appreciate that, Tomiji," Kurita said before he left the bridge of the battleship Yamato.

By this same late evening of October 24, Admiral Shoji Nishimura's van section of 2nd Striking Force had reached Surigao Strait with its two battleships, a cruiser, and several destroyers. Nishimura considered himself fortunate thus far and he hoped to clear the strait soon and arrive at Leyte Gulf at 0430 hours, October 25. He now believed that he had successfully avoided American air units and surface ships.

But, at 2300 hours, a fleet of American PT boats from Kossel Roads on the southern tip of Bohol Island spotted the van section of 2nd Striking Force. The PT squadron attempted to attack Nishimura's fleet, but the guns from the southern force easily drove off the mosquito boats. Nishimura then called Admiral Kurita.

"We are successfully passing Bohol Island and we will reach our destination in Leyte Gulf on time. Admiral Shima's rear section of the 2nd Striking Force is some 60 miles astern and he should also arrive on schedule."

"We have increased speed," Kurita answered, "And we too should be at Leyte Gulf on schedule."

But, if Admiral Nishimura easily brushed off the PT boats, he would not so easily brush off the battleships of the 7th Fleet. When Admiral Kinkaid learned of the Japanese fleet entering Surigao Strait south of Leyte, he sent his South Attack Force of the 7th Fleet to the mouth of Surigao Gulf to intercept. This American task force of the 7th Fleet included six battleships, a dozen cruisers, and a dozen destroyers. Further, two of the battleships and six of the cruisers possessed radar controlled guns for maximum accuracy. And, by October of 1944, American sailors had learned well the art of night naval combat, a far cry from those early days in the Solomons when the Japanese navy controlled the sea during the dark hours. U. S. sailors and ships were now superior in night fighting tactics.

Between 0200 and 0345 hours, on the morning of October 25, the powerful U. S. South Attack Force of the 7th Fleet chopped to pieces Admiral Nishimura's 2nd Striking Force. First down was battleship Fuso, then heavy cruiser Mogami, then destroyers Michishio, Asagumo, and Yamagumo; then the American gunners sank flag battleship Yamashiro, taking Admiral Nishimura and half of the crew to the bottom with the battleship.

The nearly two hour engagement ended in almost

total destruction for the van segment of 2nd Striking Force. Not a single American ship had been sunk, and only the Japanese destroyer Shigure escaped the holocaust before she limped swiftly westward to meet the oncoming rear section of 2nd Striking Force. When Admiral Kiyohide Shima learned what happened to the van section of this southern Japanese force, he made a wise decision.

"Reverse course. It is evident that we cannot penetrate Surigao Strait against such a formidable enemy battleship force."

"Yes, Honorable Shima," an aide said.

At 0400 hours another PT squadron from Kossel Roads saw Shima's smaller rear section fleet of 2nd Striking Force barreling westward towards the Sulu Sea. The Japanese fleet was moving quite swiftly, obviously giving up any attempt to reach Leyte Gulf.

Meanwhile, Admiral Bull Halsey had received a reconn report on the Japanese mobile carrier fleet, the northern force under Admiral Jisaburo Ozawa. This fleet was apparently steaming south towards the Philippine Sea east of Luzon. Admiral Ozawa, when he knew the American reconn plane had found him, lured Halsey even more by sending out a night air attack against the powerful American carrier fleet. The 3rd Fleet commander took the bait. His fast carrier fleet was then 360 miles northeast of Leyte, and during the early hours of October 25 he ordered his entire naval force, every carrier and every escort, to steam northward on a 260 degree course to intercept Ozawa's carrier fleet.

"By mid morning, we'll have them," Bull Halsey gloated.

Admiral Thomas Kinkaid also saw an opportunity to send more Japanese ships to the bottom. When the U. S. 7th Fleet commander heard that the remnants of 2nd Striking Force was returning swiftly westward towards the Sulu Sea, he moved at once. He sent the bulk of his fleet on a swift western course through Surigao Strait to catch the Japanese cripples of Admiral Nishimura's battered fleet.

Thus, by the early morning of October 25, the powerful 3rd Fleet would be far to the north chasing Ozawa's northern force, while the bulk of the 7th Fleet would be far to the west in the Sulu Sea to catch the survivors of the Japanese 2nd Striking Force. Halsey was certain his pilots had macerated and driven off what was left of the fleet trying to make San Bernadino Strait (1st Striking Force); Kinkaid was just as certain that only cripples remained of the second Japanese fleet (2nd Striking Force). And, since Halsey's powerful carriers were now after the Japanese mobile fleet, the northern force, neither Halsey nor Kinkaid worried about Leyte Gulf.

Only U. S. Taffy 3, a CVE unit of six jeep carriers lay off Leyte Gulf. The small force, with a complement of about a hundred planes, had as a screen a mere three destroyers and four destroyer escorts. They alone stood outside of Leyte Gulf when 1st Striking Force at 0500 hours, October 25, 1944, cleared San Bernadino Strait and steamed south off the east coast of Samar towards Leyte Gulf. Taffy 3 would face an impossible task—a confrontation with the "destroyed" 1st Striking Force: four battleships, six big cruisers, two light cruisers, and eleven destroyers.

Chapter Three

At 0500 hours, October 25, 1944, no sailor among the complement of Taffy 3 expected anything more than some Japanese aerial nusiance raids on this day. The small jeep carrier unit included baby flat tops USS Gambier Bay, Kalinin Bay, Kitkun Bay, St. Lo, White Plains, and flag Fanshaw Bay, with a total of about 125 aircraft, half fighters and half Avenger and Dauntless bombers. The jeep carrier screen included destroyers USS Hoel, Johnson, Flag Heermann, and destroyer escorts USS Dennis, John Butler, Raymond, and Samuel Roberts.

The commander of Taffy 3, Admiral Clifton "Ziggy" Sprague, was probably the biggest worry wart in the U. S. Navy. From the day he entered Roxbury Latin School in Boston in 1896, Sprague worried constantly: about his grades, his athletic prowess, his deportment, and his social relationships with school mates. But, he became an honor student and a good football player, two attributes that won him an appointment to Annapolis. Still, when he entered the U. S. Naval Academy, he worried again: mastering the subject matter, fulfilling his duties, relationships with others. But again he excelled, graduating among the top ten of his class. Perhaps in the case of Ziggy Sprague, perpetual worry had given him an unconscious push to succeed.

In 1918, the navy had assigned the round faced, barrel shaped Ziggy Sprague to gunboat Wheeling to finish out World War I. He had then served on the battleship USS Tennessee before he qualified as a naval aviator. Fellow tars often wondered why Sprague had joined naval aviation, a quite new field, since he worried so much about success. But Sprague again excelled. At the naval aviation station in Hampton Roads, he designed an arresting gear for a carrier deck to retrieve planes. The design had no doubt saved many lives.

Clifton Sprague's first command was the seaplane tender Tampin at Pearl Harbor, and his vessel was the first to fire back at the Japanese on that Day of Infamy, December 7, 1941. Immediately after Pearl Harbor, he was promoted to Captain and given command of the carrier USS Wasp. When he became an admiral in August of 1944, he won command of Taffy 3, an escort jeep carrier unit.

Sprague, like Admiral Kurita, was a dedicated navy man, quiet and retiring, who rarely smiled or raised his voice. But, since he always considered foremost the safety of his sailors and pilots, those under him held Sprague in the highest esteem.

Taffy 3 had drawn a secondary role for Operation King II, the Philippines invasion. The unit maintained combat air patrols (CAP), flew antisubmarine patrols, and supported ground troops who were pushing out from the beaches to engage the enemy in the Leyte hills. By 0530 on the morning of October 25, word reached Ziggy Sprague that all enemy surface ship threats to Leyte Gulf had ended. The Japanese fleets trying to clear San Bernadino Strait and the Surigao Strait had been destroyed or driven off, with cripples fleeing westward. Halsey's fast carrier fleet had spotted the Japanese carrier fleet and was now chasing this third enemy fleet northward. So, for one of the few times in World War II, worry wart Sprague relaxed on the bridge of the Taffy 3 flagship, jeep carrier Fanshaw Bay.

With emerging dawn, Taffy 3 went about its routine business while the jeep carriers wallowed off the coast of Samar, northeast of Leyte Gulf. CVE White Plains launched aircraft with the first light of day, sending 16 aircraft aloft to attack cripples of the Japanese fleet in the Sulu Sea. CVE White Plains sent out another 12 planes to support army ground troops on Leyte. At 0600 hours, 24 aircraft left the deck of St. Lo to also chase after Nishimura's battered remnants of the 2nd Striking Force. Twelve aircraft from Fanshaw Bay had left the CVE's deck for the usual morning antisubmarine patrols.

At 0603, with daylight brightening the eastern horizon of the Pacific, Admiral Clifton Ziggy Sprague leisurely drank coffee on the bridge of Fanshaw Bay. He stared to the north at the three destroyers and four DE's that moved slowly back and forth as a screen for his jeep carriers, mostly to protect the baby flat tops from Japanese submarines. Other sailors aboard the six jeep carriers felt equally at ease on this quiet morning, with patches of rain squall clouds overhead.

Certainly, neither the American sailors of Taffy 3 nor the sailors about the countless auxiliary ships in Leyte Gulf, and more specifically San Pedro Bay, feared any surface ship or carrier plane attacks from the Japanese on this calm morning. In fact, at 0614 hours, Admiral Ziggy Sprague ordered all Taffy 3 vessels to secure from general quarters, to set condition three, and to sail into Leyte Gulf from their night time station off Samar. Deck crews settled down to breakfast before they resumed their morning routine.

Aboard the bridge of Fanshaw Bay, a radioman brought a message to Captain James Carsen, the Taffy 3 Chief of Staff. Carsen brought the report to Admiral Sprague. "All air units have been launched, Sir. CAP's and anti-submarine patrols as well as Leyte support flights are out. Aircraft from White Plains and St. Lo are on the way to the Sulu Sea to help in the hunt for those Japanese survivors of that battle in the Surigao Strait last night."

Sprague nodded and then squinted into the early morning. "No more signs of any enemy surface ships?"

"None, Sir," Captain Carsen answered.

"Do we have search planes out?"

"Yes, Sir, a half dozen PBY's," Carsen said. "They're patrolling both Surigao Strait to the south and San Bernadino Strait to the north. Thus far, they haven't seen anything. We've got to assume there are no Japanese ships in this area."

Clifton Sprague nodded and then took another sip of coffee.

Fifty miles to the north, Admiral Takeo Kurita's 1st Striking Force was now sailing southward towards Leyte Gulf on a 170 degree course at a leisurely 20 knots. He had already cleared San Bernadino Strait some hours ago, so PBY's would not see his fleet. Kurita stood on the bridge of Yamato, drinking tea and nibbling a rice cake. He squinted into the brightening morning while his communications officer, Cmdr. Masataki Okimuya, stood on one side of him, while his chief of staff, Admiral Tomiji Koyanagi, stood on the other side of him. Koyanagi peered through binoculars and then turned to face the 1st Striking Force commander.

"We see nothing to the south, Honorable Kurita."

"Nothing? No sign of enemy vessels?"

"None, Sir," Koyanagi shook his head.

Kurita nodded, took another sip of tea, and then looked at the helmsman. "Are we maintaining our 170 degree course?"

"Yes, Admiral."

Now Kurita looked at Cmdr. Okimuya. "Have we heard further from Admiral Nishimura? Has the 2nd Striking Force beaten off the enemy and made the strait?"

"We have heard nothing for two hours," Okimuya said.

"We must know what has happened to 2nd Striking Force, and we must know for certain what kind of enemy combat fleet is guarding Leyte Gulf."

Yamato's commander, Admiral Matome Ugaki,

suddenly looked at Kurita. "I will launch search planes at once." When Kurita nodded, Ugaki picked up his radio phone to order catapult of two scout planes.

Kurita himself, sipped the last of his tea, put down the cup on a nearby table, and then peered through the forward window of the bridge at the low, gloomy morning clouds that might dump another rain squall over the sea at any moment. Kurita next looked straight ahead where two cruisers of Crudiv 5, Haguro and Chokai, sailed leisurely. To the left, on the forward starboard, sailed Desron 10 with its light cruiser Yahagi and seven destroyers under the command of Admiral Susumu Kimura. The squadron plied some 2,000 yards south, southwest of battleship Yamato. Besides cruiser Yahagi, Desron 10 included destroyers Nowaki, Kiyoshima, Urakaze, Yukikaze, Hamakaze, Isokaze, and Fujinami. Kurita then turned to his communications officer. "Have you heard from Admiral Kimura?"

"Yes, Honorable Kurita," Okimuya said. "He reports that Desron 10 is on course, but their observers have not yet seen any sign of the enemy to the south."

Kurita nodded and walked to the port side of the bridge to stare out of the port window at battleships Kongo and Hurana off the port aft. The Batdiv 3 ships moved in tandem, 1,000 yards apart. Directly abeam of Yamato on this port side was Admiral Kuzutaka Shiraishi's Crudiv 7: Flag Kumano, Chikuma, Tone, and Suzuya. Finally in the distant port side, beyond Crudiv 7, sailed Desron 2: light cruiser Noshiro and destroyers Kishinami, Naganami, and Okinami.

Kurita was satisfied. All units were in proper formation, the same disposition he had assumed throughout the night. But, he was still surprised. Despite the 1st Striking Force's close proximity to Leyte Gulf, and despite the full emergence of daylight, no one in the Japanese fleet had yet seen a sign of the enemy. Either the Americans were utterly complacent, or there were no surface or carrier fleets outside of Leyte Gulf to oppose Kurita's sail along the east coast of Samar. Since the air attacks yesterday, the Japanese fleet had made 150 miles in seven hours without American interference. Kurita and his staff, in fact, had been astonished to find no American fleet units to meet him at the east entrance of San Bernadino Strait.

The final, successful sail through the strait had followed an uneasy night. At 0230, Kurita had received a message from Admiral Nishimura. American torpedo boats had spotted the 2nd Striking Force as Nishimura steered eastwards toward Surigao Strait. Then, at 0335, another message from Nishimura: they had sighted three enemy ships. Next, after two hours of silence, a message had come from Admiral Kiyohide Shima of the tandem rear division of 2nd Striking Force. The message had indicated that Nishimura had come under heavy attack by American warships.

Then, a message had come at 0432 hours from Admiral Shima: Nishimura was fully engaged in a night battle with an enemy fleet. But, Shima's communication of 0432 hours had been the last message, and Kurita did not know if 2nd Striking Force had overcome the enemy opposition and continued through Surigao Strait, or whether Nishimura had turned back. Despite all efforts, Cmdr. Okimuya had been unable to raise either Nishimura or Shima.

Still, despite his ignorance on the fate of the 2nd Striking Force, Kurita had continued his sail on a No. 19 alert cruising disposition. He had safely navigated the narrow San Bernadino Strait with the help of a bright moon that shone through high clouds and by 0500 hours, Kurita had made the strait and altered course on his present 170 degree heading, moving through the sea some ten miles off the east coast of Samar. Kurita expected to reach Leyte Gulf at 1000 hours and rendezvous with Nishimura at a point ten miles east of Saluan Island, directly east of Leyte Gulf. The two fleets would then move into the gulf for their heavy surface ship bombardment.

Meanwhile, Japanese patrol planes from Admiral Fukudome's 2nd Air Fleet had flown over the Leyte Gulf area all during the night of October 24-25 and had reported four enemy ship concentrations in the gulf. Unfortunately, 2nd Air Fleet headquarters in Manila did not pass the information on to Admiral Kurita, and Kurita knew nothing of the patrol plane sightings. After the 1st Striking Force commander scanned the disposition of his fleet, he turned to Admiral Koyanagi.

"I am confused. Surely, the Americans should have observed us by now."

"I do not understand, either." Admiral Koyanagi answered. He peered through his own binoculars to the south, but saw nothing except the lighter Japanese warships up ahead. Then, he picked up his radio phone and called Admiral Susumu Kimura, commander of the vanguard Desron 10.

"Have you observed enemy surface or carrier vessels?"

"We have still seen nothing," Kimura answered. "It is my belief that any enemy vessels are sheltered inside of Leyte Gulf."

"My own feelings," Admiral Koyanagi said. "Still, do they not even have observation aircraft aloft?"

"We have not seen such enemy aircraft," Kimura said.

"Very well," the 1st Striking Force chief of staff said. "Maintain the 170 degree course at 20 knots."

"Yes, Admiral."

Now, Admiral Tomiji Koyanagi returned to the bridge table where a steward had brought more tea for the officers. Then, Kurita, Koyanagi, and Ugaki sat down to the refreshments. The three admirals simply could not understand why American aircraft had not seen their big fleet heading south. The Japanese officers sat silently for a full minute, when Cmdr. Okimuya approached the commander of 1st Striking Force.

"Honorable Kurita, a radio message from the Honorable Ozawa."

Kurita took the sheet of paper, read, nodded, and then looked at his fellow officers. "Admiral Ozawa has successfully drawn to the north the powerful American fast carrier fleet. The latest observation report from Ozawa's scout aircraft indicates that the American fleet is now at a latitude of 15.1 north and longitude of 124.0 west. The enemy task force is thus three hours or more to the north of us."

"Then the Honorable Ozawa has done his job well," Admiral Ugaki grinned. "We can be certain that no aircraft from this Yankee fast carrier force can interfere with our sortie into Leyte Gulf."

Kurita pursed his lips. "Still, we cannot be certain that all elements of this massive enemy carrier fleet has joined in the pursuit of Admiral Ozawa. This American fleet reportedly includes more than a dozen huge carriers and I cannot believe that the American commander of this fleet has taken all these carriers with him to leave Leyte Gulf unguarded. Some of these carriers may still be near Leyte with supporting battleships and cruisers."

Admiral Ugaki rose from the table and peered out of the port window of the bridge to stare at the big orange sun now rising over the horizon. He looked at the broken cloud sky and then turned to Cmdr. Okimuya. "And there is still no report of enemy aircraft, Commander?"

"None, Admiral, none," the communications officer said.

"Strange, strange indeed," Ugaki shook his head. He then returned to the tea table. "We face an enigma, Takeo. Could the American admiral have been so neglectful as to take his entire fleet northward and leave nothing at Leyte Gulf?"

"You must remember, Matome," Admiral Koyanagi gestured, "the Americans have an obsession to attack aircraft carriers. The very Sho-I plan depended on this belief. If the Americans do indeed have a blind urge to destroy aircraft carriers, then it is quite possible that the American commander of the huge, fast carrier fleet did indeed take every

48

carrier and navy aircraft with him to pursue the northern force of Admiral Ozawa. Perhaps they believe they have successfully destroyed or crippled or driven off both our own fleet and that of Admiral Nishimura. Perhaps they believe there was no longer any need to keep aircraft carriers and big battleships about Leyte Gulf. Remember, we did not even see so much as a torpedo boat patrolling the entrance to San Bernadino Strait."

Kurita took a sip of tea and then looked at his chief of staff. "Unless the Americans expect a second American fleet to protect the American invasion site. Could the enemy fleet of battleship and cruisers that attacked Nishimura's 2nd Striking Force last night now lie at anchor in Leyte Gulf?"

"Unfortunately, we know nothing of the American fleet's engagement with 2nd Striking Force," Admiral Ugaki said. "Perhaps such a sea battle still rages in the Surigao Strait or even in the Sulu Sea."

Kurita rose again from the table and ambled to the forward window of the bridge to peer still once more to the south. But still, he saw nothing, only the cruisers and destroyers of Crudiv 5 and Desron 10. "Fortune indeed may have favored us. Perhaps on this day we will atone for our many recent misfortunes."

On the shore of Leyte's east coast, a burst of activity had erupted by 0614 hours. The growl of 6 x 6's, of lift trucks, bulldozers, winches, and scraping caterpillars echoed about the airfield at Tacloban. Cranes on big ships in San Pedro Bay had resumed loading supplies into smaller Higgins boats that then puttered ashore. Here, loading hoists transferred the supplies from the boats to 6 x 6 trucks that growled away to deliver such supplies to a multitude of army units scattered about Leyte. Seabees still busily constructed wharfs to facilitate the unloading process.

At the Tacloban airfield construction site, Major Richard Davidson of the 305th Airdrome Engineer Battalion directed his construction crews who were working on the new airstrip. He watched two bulldozers spreading mounds of dirt before scrappers leveled off the runway, and heavy rollers tamped down the earth. Other bulldozers shaped the shoulders of the runway to assure proper drainage. A parade of dump trucks continually dropped tons of earth on the airstrip that would soon base Army Air Force planes and Marine Air Force planes, land based aircraft that would come to Leyte as soon as engineers had readied the field.

Major Richardson had finished breakfast about 0600 and he now ambled along the work areas with a subordinate, Captain Brad Whitemore. The two men watched a dump truck deposit coral on a smoothed section of the runway, before rollers crushed and smoothed the coral over the soft dirt base.

"I'm glad you got them going early, Brad," Davidson said.

"Well," Whitemore grinned, "we've been getting heat from everybody—General Whitehead, General Kenney, and General Mitchell of the 1st Marine Air Wing. The army air force boys want those P-38's of the 375th Fighter Group up here as soon as possible and General Mitchell wants to bring in his

Dauntlesses and Hellcats as soon as he can. We got two calls yesterday from 5th Air Force down in Morotai, asking the same questions: how are we doing? When will the airstrip be ready? Whitehead wants his land based planes in here as soon as we tell him it's safe enough to land."

"It's a good thing General Kenney got the navy guys to move that stuff off Calaison Point," Davidson said.

The 305th Airdrome Engineer commander then watched a huge scrapper growl past him, leveling off another mound of gravel dumped from a truck. Then, the major turned to his subordinate. "What about the Marston matting?"

"They're unloading the steel matting this morning on Depot D," Whitemore answered.

"Do you think we can lay the matting tomorrow?"

Whitemore squinted at the gloomy clouds overhead. "If we don't get too many squalls in the next 24 hours."

"How about ammo dumps?"

"Lt. Worrad says the dumps are pretty full," Whitemore answered. "We've got stacks of 500 and thousand pounders, both here and down in Dulag. God knows how many crates of strafing belts we have."

"Then planes can bomb up as soon as they get here?"

"According to Worrad, they can," the captain answered.

"I just hope to hell we don't get a Japanese air strike on those dumps," Major Davidson said. "Christ, they sent enough planes here yesterday."

"But they didn't do much damage," Whitemore said. "Those navy Hellcats and Corsairs did a good job on those Nip bombers. With navy CAP over Leyte Gulf right now, those Nips will have a hard time trying to send more bombers here."

"I don't like it," Davidson shook his head. "We had the whole fast carrier fleet here yesterday. Now, we've only got six little jeep carriers with less than 150 planes—that isn't much. And I heard that Admiral Sprague sent half of them to the west this morning to hit cripples from that Japanese fleet that tried to make Surigao Strait last night. Sprague should have kept every plane he had right here to protect Leyte. You never know what those Japs are likely to do." The major looked at the partly cloudy skies. "I'll feel a lot safer when those army P-38's and A-20 light bombers get up here from 5th Air Force."

Whitemore shrugged. "Halsey isn't worried. They knocked out those Japanese fleets that tried to reach Leyte Gulf and he figures Admiral Sprague has enough planes on those jeep carriers to take care of any more Japanese land based planes the Nips may send over Leyte."

Still, Major Richard Davidson felt uneasy. All reports indicated the Japanese fleets had been macerated. Further, the 6th American Army infantry troops were making excellent headway in their ground war. But, there were too many mounds of supplies on the beaches, too many ships in the bay, and too much activity at Dulag and Tacloban. These were unusually fat targets. If the Japanese decided to send massive formations over Leyte

52

again they could do a lot of damage with only the few fighter planes from Taffy 3 to intercept such enemy aircraft.

Then, one of the caterpillars suddenly stopped before the major and a burly sergeant leaned from the open side of the big scrapper. "Major, they ain't bringin' coral fast enough to cover this strip. They got us sittin' idle half the time."

"We've only got so many trucks, Sergeant," Davidson answered. "We've tried to make this airstrip construction our first priority, but they can't give us everything on wheels. You'll have to do the best you can."

"Yes Sir," the sergeant said before he revved the heavy engine of his 'cat and growled off.

Richard Davidson now turned to his subordinate. "Captain, maybe you ought to drive down to Dulag and see how things are going there. If we at least assure Old Man Whitehead that we're moving right along, he might not give us so much heat."

Davidson had barely returned to his headquarters hut when navy lieutenant Russell Forrester, the 1st Marine Wing liaison officer, walked into his quarters. "Major, you're moving too slow," Forrester said. "General Mitchell wants his Corsairs and Dauntlesses here within the next couple of days."

"The strip might be ready by then," Davidson said.

"The general is on my back," Forrester continued. "He got real upset after those strikes yesterday, and he thinks the Nips will start hitting us again with land based planes out of Clark and Nichols fields."

"He doesn't have much faith in the jeep carriers, does he?" Davidson grinned.

"Neither do I," Forrester said. Then he sighed. "What am I supposed to tell the general if he presses me again?"

"Tell him to send me a hundred more dump trucks," Davidson answered. "I had a sergeant belly-aching just a few minutes ago because they've got their 'cats sitting idle for lack of coral. Trucks aren't bringing the stuff in fast enough. But, if we don't get heavy rains today, we'll start laying Marston matting strips tomorrow and you can probably bring in your Dauntlesses in a couple of days."

"Okay," Lt. Forrester said.

Meanwhile, Admiral Takeo Kurita's 1st Striking Force came within 30 miles of Ziggy Sprague's Taffy 3 escort carrier force. Sprague, at ease now, relaxed on the bridge of the CVE Fanshaw Bay. He drank another cup of coffee, and he ate two fresh rolls from the jeep carrier's galley.

At 0645 hours, lookouts aboard Fanshaw Bay heard antiaircraft to the north. The ack-ack puzzled the American sailors. Were Taffy 3's screen of three destroyers and four destroyer escorts firing at friendly planes again? Perhaps firing at returning PBY reconn aircraft that American gunners so often mistook for Japanese Emily flying boats? Only moments later, the men in the radar room of Fanshaw Bay got blips on their screen — unidentified surface ship contacts. At almost the same moment, men in the CVE's radio room picked up on the inter-fighter direction net some heavy, garbled Japanese chatter. Surely, there were no Japanese ships in the area. Halsey's 3rd Fleet had utterly decimated the 1st Striking Force that had tried to make San Bernadino Strait and Admiral Kinkaid's battleship-cruiser force had destroyed the 2nd Striking Force trying to make Surigao Strait.

Even as Admiral Sprague, Captain Carsen and Captain Johnson on the bridge of Fanshaw Bay studied these strange audio reports, they got a clear, unmistakable message from Ensign Bill Jensen, a Fanshaw Bay Hellcat pilot who was out on anti-submarine patrol. Jensen, far to north, radioed a stunning report at 0647 hours.

"Four Japanese battleships, eight cruisers, and about a dozen destroyers; they're 20 to 30 miles north of Taffy 3 position; sailing directly south at 20 to 25 knots."

"Are you sure? Are you certain?" Captain Carsen asked anxiously.

"Yes Sir, Captain," Ensign Jensen answered. "I made a low glide over one of the cruisers, and they responded with a skyful of ack-ack fire."

"It's got to be a mistake," the Taffy 3 Chief of Staff said. "It can't be Japanese. There aren't any Jap ships around. Are you sure you didn't run into some of TF 38's escort screen?"

But, a moment later, a call came from the observer in Fanshaw Bay's crow nest. "Enemy cruisers and battleships! Cruisers and battleships! Bearing, 170 degrees." The observer had seen the unmistakable pagoda masts of Japanese heavy warships.

Admiral Clifton Ziggy Sprague, Captain Dick Johnson, and Captain James Carsen looked at each other in astonishment. If worry wart Ziggy Sprague ever found reason to fret, he had certainly found reason now, at 0647 hours, October 25, 1944.

"Son of a bitch," Sprague finally cursed. "Halsey and Kinkaid left us bare assed."

Chapter Four

If the Americans expressed shock at the sudden arrival of a powerful Japanese fleet, the Japanese also expressed surprise. Kurita and his staff had been ignorant of anything to the south since their last communication from Admiral Shima, when the rear section commander of 2nd Striking Force told Kurita at 0432 hours that Nishimura was engaging an American fleet in Surigao Gulf. Further, Kurita had yet to receive any message from Admiral Shigeru Fukudome, whose 2nd Air Fleet headquarters had been receiving Kurita's message, while Manila's own communications could not, apparently, reach the 1st Striking Force.

Everybody from Kurita down to galley stewards could only conjecture on the complement of the enemy fleet to the south. Unfortunately, the first visual sighting of American ships revealed the clear shape of aircraft carriers, and near panic gripped the uneasy Japanese who had suffered considerably from American carrier planes yesterday. Had 1st Striking Force run into the fast American carrier fleet again? Were the reports of this fleet supposedly

57

chasing Ozawa quite false? Was this powerful U. S. carrier fleet, in fact, still wallowing around Leyte Gulf instead of pursuing Ozawa's mobile fleet to the north?

Most of the Japanese sailors in Kurita's fleet were inclined to believe that the carriers to the south were indeed part of the American powerful fast carrier fleet. The Japanese now suspected they had merely been engaged in wishful thinking. Surely, the Americans would not be so stupid as to leave Leyte Gulf unprotected.

Kurita himself was among those who sighted Ensign Jensen's scout plane in his glide dive before the U. S. pilot dropped depth charges. Kurita did not know the plane was an antisubmarine patrol aircraft from a baby flat top. Now, Kurita peered hard through the forward window of Yamato's bridge and he then turned to Admiral Ugaki.

"Have the scout planes yet determined the complement of this enemy force?"

"We have had no reports, Takeo."

Kurita turned to his communications officer. "You must get a report from Admiral Kimura of Desron 10."

"At once, Admiral," Cmdr. Okimuya answered.

In the event Kurita needed to engage enemy carrier planes, Kurita had planned to deploy his forces in columnar cruising formation by altering course from his 170 degree bearing to a 110 degree circular antiaircraft formation. All hands in 1st Striking Force had anticipated at best only some surface ship opposition when they heard that Ozawa had lured away the American fast carrier force.

But now, the shock of sighting aircraft carriers brought illusionary sightings from sailors on the cruisers and destroyers.

Lookouts throughout the 1st Striking Force flooded the radio room of flagship Yamato with exaggerated reports. Some observers claimed they had seen heavy cruisers shuttling back and forth in a screen for the American carriers, ships that in reality were mere DD's and DDE's, destroyers and destroyer escorts. Other Japanese observers reported the baby flat tops of Taffy 3 as big, fast carriers of the U. S. 3rd Fleet that could launch hundreds of planes. Some of the lookouts had even reported two battleships.

Admiral Ugaki, utilizing powerful field glasses, stared hard at the carriers that now stirred frantically over the surface of the choppy Philippine Sea.

"Have you identified the enemy carriers, Matome?" Kurita asked anxiously. "Are they of the big Independence class American carriers?"

"I am not certain, Takeo," Ugaki answered. "I have never seen such vessels before. Perhaps they are a new class of carrier the Americans have recently brought into the Pacific."

Ugaki and other observers were not familiar with the profile of the American escort carriers that had been fashioned from tanker hulls. So, the suspicions grew: 1st Striking Force had run into a large U. S. fast carrier fleet.

Nonetheless, Admiral Takeo Kurita reacted swiftly, perhaps too swiftly. He looked anxiously at the men about him and then made a quick decision.

"It does not matter what kind of American fleet lies ahead of us. We will not lose this heaven sent opportunity to attack an enemy carrier fleet. We will destroy at once their flight decks and then destroy the remainder of the American task force." He looked at Admiral Koyanagi. "Issue an order at once: all vessels will commence fire; a general attack."

"But Admiral," Koyanagi said, "we have not formed proper columnar formation for a coordinated attack and defense against aircraft."

"We must attack while the opportunity is here, especially since we can already see the American carriers launching aircraft. We cannot waste a moment."

"Yes Admiral," Koyanagi answered. At 0650 hours, the order went out to all vessels of 1st Striking Force: General attack! Commence fire!

Admiral Susumu Kimura, commander of the lead Desron 10, upped his speed to 22 knots and shot forward to start shooting at the jeep carriers from 25,000 yards. Admiral Kazutaka Shiraishi of Crudiv 7, meanwhile, hurried forward with his heavy cruisers to also start pummelling the American jeep carriers with massive 8" shells.

Admiral Clifton Sprague of Taffy 3 issued orders as soon as he was certain the Japanese fleet was bearing down on his baby flat tops. At 0657, he ordered a course change of due east—to windward, in order to launch aircraft and to open range from the Japanese fleet barrelling southward: He also ordered increased speed to full flank of 17½ knots. Then, he ordered his DD's and DDE's to make smoke that could hide his carriers.

Next, the Taffy 3 commander ordered his CVE's into a rough oval some 2,500 yards in diameter. In the new formation, flagship Fanshaw Bay and CVE White Plains sailed on the northward exposed flank. St. Lo and Kitkun Bay sailed on the southward flank, while Gambier Bay took the point and Kalinin Bay followed to the rear of the oval formation.

Then, Ziggy Sprague got on the radio. "This is Taffy 3! Taffy 3! We're under attack by a powerful enemy battleship-cruiser fleet. We need help. All the help we can get. Anybody! Send help!"

Admiral Thomas Kinkaid, aboard the 7th Fleet's transport flagship Wasatch in Leyte Gulf received the message from Sprague in utter astonishment. His battleships were to the westward, on the other side of Surigao Strait and chasing Japanese cripples in the Sulu Sea. Kinkaid could not get these capital ships back for at least three hours. Still, he quickly called his South Attack Force and ordered this fleet back to Leyte Gulf with all possible speed.

Far to the north, aboard the 3rd Fleet's flag New Jersey, Admiral William Bull Halsey received the report of the enemy fleet off Samar with total horror, along with pangs of agonizing guilt. He had held the responsibility of guarding San Bernadino Strait. But, in his certainty that all enemy fleets had been destroyed, he had not left so much as a picket destroyer to keep an eye on San Bernadino Strait. Now, the jeep carriers of Taffy 3 and dozens of ships in Leyte Gulf were in danger of annihilation.

Halsey did the only thing he could. He ordered Task Force 38.3 under Admiral Fred Sherman to about face and hurry back to Leyte Gulf with Sherman's four battleships. four cruisers and three fast carriers. Halsey hoped the powerful 38.3 unit could ward off total disaster for Taffy 3 and Leyte Gulf.

The only hopeful response from Admiral Sprague's pleas came from Admiral William Sample, deputy commander of the southern Taffy escort carrier groups, Taffy 1 and Taffy 2. The several jeep carriers of the southern Taffy groups lay some 150 miles to the south of Taffy 3. "Don't get your ass in an uproar," Admiral Sample answered Ziggy Sprague's pleas. "We've got a lot of planes out chasing those Japanese cripples west of Surigao Strait, but we've still got another hundred around. We'll launch aircraft as soon as we can. Just don't do anything rash; and don't get yourself too excited—bad for your heart."

"Hell, that's easy for you to say," Sprague answered. "You're not taking hits from goddamn cruisers and battleships."

"We'll have planes there in an hour or two," Sample said.

"We may be at the bottom by then."

"Just hang on; make smoke; run in circles."

"Sure, sure," Sprague grumbled. "Just get those goddamn planes up here as fast as you can."

"Have you launched your own planes yet?"

"We've starting launching now," Sprague said.

Most of the jeep carrier commanders of Taffy 3 did not wait for Admiral Sprague's orders to launch planes. The verified approach of the Japanese fleet had prompted every baby flat top captain to launch immediately. Captain Jim Whitney of CVE Kitkun

Bay ordered all planes off at once. His air commander of Composite Squadron 5, Cmdr. Bob Fowler, reacted quickly. He would leave with his full complement of planes, 16 torpedo bombers and 12 FM-2 fighter planes. But, the sudden onset of the Japanese fleet had ruled out time to load these planes with the few torpedoes available. Deck crews hastily loaded the Avengers with hundred pound bombs and 5" rockets. Other deck crews barely had time to load strafing belts into the 12 Hellcats.

In fact, Kitkun Bay had barely turned into the wind to launch planes when the first whooshing salvo of shellfire from the Japanese cruiser Yahagi splashed yellow geysers in the water around the jeep carrier.

"What the hell happens if we don't have a ship when we get back?" Lt. Walter Crocker asked Cmdr. Fowler.

"How the hell do I know," Fowler answered. "Let's just hope the carrier is still here after we make our air strike."

"Some strike," Crocker scowled, "16 goddamn planes with hundred pounders. What the hell are we gonna do with that against big cruisers and battleships?"

"The best we can," Fowler answered before he climbed into the cockpit of his Avenger with his two fellow crew members. His gunner, Sergeant Jim Van Brunt, looked in awe at the splashing, colored geysers of 8" shells concussioning in the sea with rattling explosions. The gunner wondered if his Avenger would even clear the deck before one of the shells hit the CVE squarely. But, a moment later, the Avenger was off and soaring skyward. Van Brunt sighed in relief, momentarily forgetting that he would now fly into a barrage of heavy ack-ack fire from Japanese battle wagons and cruisers.

Fortunately for Kitkun Bay, all 28 aircraft got off by 0710 hours, some 20 minutes after the Japanese bombardment began. Miraculously, not one shell had struck Kitkun Bay during the aircraft launch, the jeep cruiser suffering only minor damage from near miss shell fragments.

On fellow jeep carrier Kalinin Bay, captain Tom Williamson, like Captain Jim Whitney, also ordered all planes aloft. Air commander Bill Keighley of the carrier's Composite Squadron 3 had scrambled himself, his pilots, and his crews to 8 Avengers and 12 Hellcats, the only available combat ready planes. Once more, deck crews found no time to load torpedoes and only two of the planes carried them. In fact, launch crews had barely raised the aircraft to the flight deck before the helmsman of Kalinin Bay steered the CVE eastward into the wind to launch planes that again carried mere 100 pound bombs and 5" rockets.

"Jesus, Bill," Lt. Pat Capano said to Cmdr. Bill Keighley, "do you think we'll get these planes off the deck before they tear the deck apart?"

"We can only try," Keighley answered. "Just get your ass in your Hellcat."

As the Avengers, in pairs, roared down the deck and into the wind to the east, 8" cruiser shells exploded ever closer to Kalinin Bay, shooting up colored sprays: yellow from cruiser Yahagi, purple from cruiser Kumano, red from cruiser Chikuma, and green from cruiser Tone. The shells, though close, did not deter the aircraft launch. All 8 Avengers got off and 10 Hellcats got off. But, as the last two Hellcats started down the deck, an 8" shell struck the deck squarely, gouged out a huge hole, and shattered the two Hellcats, dumping the aircraft fragments and the slain pilots into the sea.

Captain Tom Williamson stared aghast. The plowing Japanese cruisers of 1st Striking Force had begun closing accurately. He now zig-zagged in an evasive run.

From the bridge of flag Fanshaw Bay, Captain David Johnson ordered his own planes airborne. "Launch! Launch! On the double!"

"Over half our planes are out on support missions, Sir," somebody yelled from the deck. "We've only got a half dozen Avengers and a half dozen Corsairs."

"Well, goddamn it, Launch!" Captain Johnson barked. "Launch them!"

"Aye, Sir."

A few moments later, six Avenger torpedo bombers and six Corsair fighter planes, already on deck in anticipation of going to Surigao Strait, wheeled into position for launch. Four of the Avengers carried torpedoes and two carried 500 pound bombs. Cmdr. Bob Roberts, in the lead Avenger, waited anxiously until the launch chief dropped his flag for take off. Within a few minutes the 12 aircraft were airborne. Hopefully, the light bombers carrying torpedoes and 500 pounders could cause some serious damage to the Japanese ships.

Aboard Gambier Bay, the last of Taffy 3's available planes revved their engines before shooting off the jeep carrier's deck. The Gambier Bay commander, Captain Bill Viewig, standing stiffly on the bridge of his CVE, shuttled his glance between the aircraft preparing for take off and the yellow, green, purple, and red shells splashing a kaleidoscope of colored geysers around Gambier Bay. Viewig did not like his forward position in the carrier formation for he was too exposed to the pursuing Japanese cruisers of Crudiv 7 and the destroyers of Desron 10.

Yet, one of the sailors on deck offered some wry humor to a companion. "The bastards! They're shootin' at us in technicolor."

The companion did not answer. He merely gaped at the horrid beauty of the colored geysers, wondering if one of them would snuff out his life at any moment.

But, the Japanese shooting was thus far inaccurate. No shell had hit the deck area before Cmdr. Ed Huxtable left the jeep carrier's deck with his 9 Dauntless dive bombers and 10 Hellcat fighters.

At 0712 hours, Admiral Ziggy Sprague called the jeep carrier commanders. "Are all planes launched?"

The baby flat top captains gave him the same answer: "Yes."

"Okay," Sprague said, "now we'll sail in a circular zig zag course, but keep to the east and south. Stay the hell out of Leyte Gulf. That's just what the nips want—get us trapped inside the gulf. Anyway, so long as they're after us, they won't try for Leyte Gulf, and maybe we can move far enough south to meet help from Sample's carriers or Kinkaid's battlewagons."

No one argued with Ziggy Sprague's logic. Despite his worry wart reputation, Sprague never faltered. The Taffy 3 commander acted with cool, methodical discipline. He knew well enough that not only his CVE's, but every ship in Leyte Gulf was in jeopardy. Ironically, his only chance to avoid a massacre in the gulf and on his own Taffy 3 was to lure the powerful Kurita fleet southward, as Ozawa had lured Admiral Bull Halsey northward.

Strangely, Admiral Takeo Kurita, the dedicated, precise, by-the-book fleet commander, failed to act with the same calm logic as did Ziggy Sprague. Kurita had neglected to keep his powerful ships in the proper No. 19 battle disposition, but had allowed them to scatter themselves all over the Philippine Sea. Now, Kurita's ships fired blindly and indiscriminately at the American jeep carriers. The quick, authoritative "general attack" order from Kurita had prompted the Japanese ship commanders to ply headlong towards the enemy with no coordinated strategy, and with each ship commander acting independently.

Battleships Yamato and Nagato of Batdiv 1 kept in column, but the two battleships of Batdiv 3, Kongo and Haruna, operated by themselves, with both ships wildly firing 14" guns without carefully singling out a specific target, or often firing at the same target. The six heavy cruisers had broken from their tandem formations, steaming off in several directions to fire 8" shells at anything they saw moving to the south. In fact, the cruisers of

Crudiv 7 and Crudiv 5 had overtaken the smaller vessels, the light cruisers and destroyers of Desron 10 and Desron 2. Astonishingly, Desron 2 had even fallen to the rear of the fleet, far out of a forward torpedo launch position.

Admiral Matome Ugaki, commander of Batdiv 1, pressed the 1st Striking Force commander to speed his destroyers ahead. "Honorable Kurita, should not the destroyer squadrons hurry forward to launch torpedoes."

"We are too far for accurate torpedo strikes," Kurita answered. "We must destroy these enemy carriers as quickly as possible with long range shell fire from our battleships and heavy cruisers."

Still, despite the now aimless formation of Kurita's fleet, the downpour of dozens of 8", 14" and 18" shells could not fail to score some hits. Even at flank speed of 17.5 knots, the CVE's could not outrun the 30 knot speed of Kurita's vessels. Further, by 0730 hours, Admiral Kazutaka Shiraishi, commander of Crudiv 7, had reformed his four cruisers on his own and he had then closed on the port quarter of Ziggy Sprague's escort carriers. Crudiv 7 soon came within 15,000 yards of tail end Kalinin Bay.

Captain Tom Williamson, the Kalinin Bay commander, could almost see the turret muzzles from these forefront cruisers and he turned to his bridge officer. "Where the hell's that smoke from our escorts? If we don't get smoke to hide us, we're dead."

"They say it's coming, Sir," the aide told the Kalinin Bay commander.

Captain Williamson felt perspiration dampen

his face for he knew he could not escape the enemy guns much longer. The Japanese cruisers were closing fast and multi-colored shells exploded ever nearer. Williamson did not expect to last another half hour if the heavy caliber cruiser fire hit home. His CVE, like the other baby flat tops of Taffy 3, had thin hulls and their armament only included one 5" gun with some 20MM and 40MM antiaircraft guns.

"Goddamnit," one of the deck hands of Kalinin Bay cursed, "how come we drew Tail End Charlie position? We'll take more fire than all those other jeep carriers combined."

"Yeh," a companion nodded. Then, he squinted northeast, looking for the DD and DDE escorts who were supposed to make smoke. "Where the hell is that smoke screen from the wolves and little wolves?"

"Coming, coming," the first man scowled disdainfully. "That's what they tell us."

Then, at 0735 hours, Kalinin Bay caughts its first hit. The shell entered the port side about two feet above the deck in the bos'n stores and blew away the compartment and three sailors. The next two shells sailed into the port side of the platform deck, ripping away bulk plates #82 and #118, rupturing a floor plate in the engine room, and pouring water into an oil drum compartment to a level of five feet before repair crews sealed the flooding. The fourth shell struck the carpenter shop, a half dozen feet above the hangar deck; then the shell passed through the elevator pit, through the starboard quarter, and plopped into the sea—a dud.

The next shell, a 14 incher, near missed, sending a huge spray of water over Kalinin Bay's deck and nearly washing a half dozen men overboard. The next shell, another 14 incher, brought the first real damage to Kalinin Bay. The shell struck the aviation armory, cut through a bulkhead, went down the platform deck, and landed in the machine shop where it exploded. The blast tore the compartment to pieces and the battered area quickly flooded to a depth of ten feet before dazed bluejackets sealed off the compartment. The same monstrous explosion started a fire below the battered machine shop and the damaged aviation armory. A horde of sailors rushed to the area to put out the flames, but no one knew if they could do so before Kalinin Bay went under from the heavy pounding.

Shell #8 exploded under the counter of the fantail and damaged the under hull of the ship along with the sprinkler system. Hit #9 also exploded on the fantail, caused more structural damage, severed cables, and blasted away the after messhall. The next salvo of shells hit the deck, ripping away a full ten foot square of plating and leaving five smaller holes. Metal splinters spewed through the officers' wardroom on the starboard side and into the forward elevator, ripping away the forward chain.

Shell #11, another 14 incher, also caused extensive damage. The shell hit the flight deck, slicing through the deck, and wrecking the I beams that supported the forward elevator. The explosion further wrecked the elevator platform, the elevator control room, and radio room II, knocking out communications and killing two sailors. Fragments from the shell blast also pierced the radar room, but did not cause injury or serious damage.

However, another shell, a new 8 incher, hit an acetylene torch near the already smashed carpenter shop, erupted an intense fire in the hangar deck, and brought more flooding that repair crews tried desperately to contain.

Shells #12, 13, 14, and 15 caused still more damage to Tail End Charlie Kalinin Bay. One hit passed through the starboard forward stack, damaged radar equipment, and started another fire. The next hit also came through the flight deck and blew away flight crew lockers, the crew's bunk room, and four I beams below deck; while the same explosion ruptured the A-308 gas pressure compartment.

The enemy's Crudiv 7 was now almost to 10,000 yards on the port of Kalinin Bay. The swift close on the jeep carrier could be attributed to Admiral Shiraishi's wise decision to form his four cruisers into proper battle order. The harried Kalinin Bay could only respond with its 5" gun, firing furiously at the nearest Japanese cruiser, flag Kumano. One of the 5 inchers did score a hit on the cruiser's #2 gun turret and a second 5" shell struck the #2 turret again to start a severe fire.

Oddly, the two hits on Kumano, especially the one causing the fire, prompted the cruiser to break off her attack on Kalinin Bay and turn to port, withdrawing from the cruiser formation—at least temporarily.

"Goddamn, we got the bastard," one of the bluejackets cried elatedly from Kalinin Bay's gun pit.

"She's gone off," a gun handler grinned. "The bitch! She can dish it out, but she can't take it."

However, the respite was brief for tail end Kalinin

Bay. Only moments later, Desron 10 closed in on the jeep carrier from the starboard quarter. Admiral Susumu Kimura, also acting on his own, had formed his light cruiser Yahagi and his seven destroyers into proper battle formation for a torpedo launch. American sailors on the jeep carrier first thought these smaller ships of Desron 10 were Taffy 3's screen of DD's and DDE's that had finally arrived to make smoke. However, the Kalinin Bay bluejackets gaped in horror when they clearly saw the high bow, two gun mounts forward, and the tripod masts of an unmistakable Japanese light cruiser—flag Yahagi.

The Desron 10 commander, Admiral Kimura, peered hard through his binoculars at the slightly aflame Kalinin Bay that now fell behind the other jeep carriers because of the many telling hits. "She appears to flounder," Kimura said.

The Yahagi commander, Captain Masi Yoshimura, nodded. "Our heavy cruisers and battleships have crippled her, Admiral. We should have little difficulty in sinking her with torpedoes."

"Increase speed," Kimura said. "When we have closed to 10,000 yards, we will launch torpedoes."

Captain Tom Williamson, from the bridge of Kalinin Bay, stared in dismay. "Oh my God! My God!" he hissed. The jeep carrier commander squinted into the sky for a sign of American planes, but he saw none under the gloomy, broken low clouds. Why hadn't U. S. planes yet made aerial assaults? Williamson ordered a zig zag to avoid a torpedo launch he was certain would come from the Japanese destroyer column. But, Williamson felt utterly depressed. Even if he avoided torpedoes, he would not likely continue to avoid gunfire from the Japanese cruisers of Crudiv 7. Williamson ordered a turn south to run from the Japanese warships as long as he could. But, Kalinin Bay was now a wounded deer trying to avoid a pack of aggressive wolves.

"Full starboard turn, full 90 degrees," Williamson cried to his helmsman.

"Aye, Sir."

Then, Williamson picked up his TBS and called Admiral Sprague in Fanshaw Bay, now far to the southeast. "Admiral, we're in big trouble. We've been hit hard and we've got three heavy cruisers and a half dozen destroyers still closing on us. We can't evade much longer. I've ordered 90 degrees to the south, southeast. Where the hell are those screen destroyers to make smoke?"

"They're making smoke as fast as they can," Sprague answered. "They should be coming past you any minute."

"Christ," Williamson complained, "they're nowhere in sight. If I don't get smoke soon, I'll be finished. I've got 18 planes out, and my deck is chopped full of holes. If I don't get time to make repairs, I'll never retrieve my planes."

"I don't know what to tell you," Sprague said, "except to evade."

"Where the hell are the aircraft?" Williamson asked. "Why haven't they attacked these enemy ships!"

"I think they've gone after the battleships," Sprague said.

"Jesus, can't we get them after these enemy cruisers? Maybe our planes can cause enough confusion to break up their attack formations."

"Call your own air unit, Tom," Sprague said. "Tell Bill Keighley I said to come back and protect your carrier."

Captain Williamson then called Cmdr. Bill Keighley. "I've got permission from the admiral to have you come back and protect Kalinin Bay. A whole destroyer column and a cruiser column are pounding hell out of us and they're still closing. Can your planes break up their battle formation?"

"I'll do what I can," Bill Keighley answered. "We should be over those enemy ships in ten or fifteen minutes."

Fifteen minutes! Kalinin Bay could be down by then. Captain Williamson again peered hard to the east, looking for the escort screen that was supposed to make smoke. But, he did not see them. Then, the Kalinin Bay skipper looked soberly at his executive officer, Cmdr. Ed Quilter. "Pipe all hands; prepare to abandon ship."

"Abandon ship, Sir?" Cmdr. Quilter gasped.

"That's what I said."

"Yes, Sir."

When the order went out, every man aboard Kalinin Bay recognized a truth: their jeep carrier was in fatal trouble, with little prospect of avoiding destruction from the Japanese Crudiv 7 column that still boomed 8" shells at the baby flat top, and from the Japanese Desron 10 column that was swiftly bearing down on them for a torpedo attack. Men aboard the jeep carrier quickly tightened life jackets around their chests, they readied rafts, and they loosened their helmets. The radio operator sent out messages everywhere—to Admiral Sprague, to the 7th Fleet flagship Wasatch in Leyte Gulf, to the airborne aircraft of Taffy 3, and even to 6th Army headquarters in Leyte: "Position, 125.9 degrees west by 14.9 degrees right. Please prepare to rescue survivors."

Captain Tom Williamson took one last look at the Japanese Desron 10 column chasing his jeep carrier and knew the enemy would soon be within range for a torpedo attack. He waited for the worst.

But then, compassionate Providence intervened. For the past 12 hours, low, thick clouds had raced across the seas and islands of the eastern Philippines, dumping occasional rain squalls. Now, at 0730 hours, the fickle tropical clouds dumped another rain squall —the worst yet. Within a single minute, a heavy wall of rain, a total curtain of water, obscured the harried Kalinin Bay. And, before the downpour ended ten minutes later, the DD's and DDE's of Taffy 3 completed their sweep with a smoke screen to totally conceal Kalinin Bay.

Admiral Susumu Kimura peered into the curtain of thick smoke and cursed. "Bakarya!"

The carrier was lost. And, aboard heavy cruiser Kumano, Crudiv 7 commander Kazutaka Shiraishi also cursed the sudden disappearance of the baby flat top. Now, both Kimura and Shiraishi would need to wait for the rain squall and the smoke screen to clear before they could resume their assault on Kalinin Bay.

Chapter Five

At 0730 hours, October 25, 1944, General Douglas MacArthur stood in the 6th Army headquarters shack at Tacloban with 6th Army commander Lt. General Walter Krueger. MacArthur was stunned by the news of a powerful Japanese battleship-cruiser fleet streaming towards Leyte Gulf along the west coast of Samar. Only last evening the SWPA commander had questioned Admiral Halsey's decision to chase the Japanese carrier fleet reported northeast of Luzon.

"Your job is to protect Leyte," MacArthur had complained.

"Our job is to keep Japanese fleets away from Leyte Gulf," Halsey had responded. "This Japanese carrier fleet represents a major threat to the invasion site, and I've got a responsibility to knock it out or to chase it off."

"But you've left nothing to protect us," MacArthur had complained further.

"We've got the Taffy escort carrier units in the area," Halsey had said. "They can take care of the few land based planes the Japanese still have. We've knocked out most of their air bases and we've destroyed hundreds of their land based planes on the ground and in the air. We've battered that Japanese fleet trying to make San Bernadino Strait and we've all but destroyed the other enemy fleet trying to make Surigao Strait. The only threat to Leyte now is that Japanese carrier fleet to the north. We intend to take care of it."

MacArthur had been unconvinced and he had howled even more when he heard that Admiral Kinkaid's battleships and cruisers of 7th Fleet had sailed southwest through Surigao Strait and into the Sulu Sea to hit Japanese cripples of the 2nd Striking Force. And finally, MacArthur had fumed again this very morning, October 25, when he learned that a horde of aircraft from the Taffy carriers had flown off to also attack Japanese cripples of the 2nd Striking Force.

But, Admiral Kinkaid had assured MacArthur. "We've still got plenty of planes to give you ground support on Leyte and to maintain CAP over Leyte. There's nothing to worry about."

However, within a half hour of the Japanese fleet sighting and its obvious threat to the Philippine invasion site, everybody in and around Leyte felt panic. Most of the army personnel doubted that Taffy 3 air units could do much, with too few planes and no heavy bombs or torpedoes to effectively hurt capital ships. The staff at 6th Army headquarters had never heard MacArthur curse as he did now—not in the Philippines in 1942, not in the retreat from Bataan, not in the fall of Corregidor, not during any Southwest Pacific campaign.

"That dumb bastard! That son of a bitch!" Mac-Arthur cursed, referring to Admiral William Bull Halsey.

Throughout two years of war in the Pacific, MacArthur and Halsey had argued over strategy, and MacArthur now felt fully justified in criticizing Halsey as an utter incompetent who had no business directing the naval aspect of the Philippine invasion. At this 0730 hour, MacArthur was sure the U. S. Navy could not stop the Japanese fleet barrelling south from San Bernadino Strait. He called Major Richard Davidson to his headquarters at once.

"Major," the SWPA commander barked, "you've got to do something. We've got to get P-38's and A-20's up here immediately. They can use skip bombs against that enemy fleet and do plenty of damage."

Davidson pursed his lips. "That's impossible, Sir. The fields at Tacloban and Dulag are simply not ready."

"We don't have to wait for the Marston matting, do we?" General Krueger asked. "We've operated planes off dirt airstrips before. You've got the runway pretty well leveled off and most of the coral crushed down."

"We don't have all the coral in yet," Davidson shook his head. "Those P-38's and A-20's are heavy; they'd bog down. We need to finish spreading and packing the coral over that airstrip before we bring in Army Air Force planes."

"How long will that be?" MacArthur asked.

"Not until mid day at the earliest," Davidson said. "Anyway, those P-38's and A-20's are still down in Morotai, seven hundred miles away. There's no way they can get up here for at least three hours."

"Goddamn it," MacArthur cursed again. "That dumb son of a bitch! That idiot! Nimitz should have known better than to put a dumb bastard like Halsey in charge of this thing."

Neither Major Richard Davidson nor General Walter Krueger answered MacArthur.

MacArthur now looked out of the 6th headquarters shack at the 'cats and 'dozers growling up and down the Tacloban runway. Then, he turned to Krueger. "Walt, we'll need to take desperate measures."

Krueger only looked at ths SWPA commander.

"You'll suspend all operations at once," MacArthur said. "Get everything that moves—trucks, jeeps, ambulances, dozers, cats, anything—and start loading them with every bit of ammo, food, and supplies they can carry. We'll start moving inland. I understand the 24th Infantry Division has secured Caragara Bay. That right?"

"Yes," Krueger answered.

"And the road from Tacloban?"

"Pretty bad, but we can make the twenty miles to Caragara Bay."

MacArthur nodded. "Okay, start packing. Maybe we can get most of our supplies, men, and vehicles out of here within a couple of hours. It's my understanding the Japanese fleet can't get here until 1000 hours at the earliest. We ought to be out of Tacloban by then."

"But General," Krueger said, "what you're asking is a tremendous job. And what about Dulag?"

"Tell them to move their asses inland, too; same as us." MacArthur looked at the huge map of Leyte pinned on the wall. "The 96th Infantry has secured Dagami and Burauen, west of Dulag, haven't they?"

"Yes."

"Then get them moving."

"General, Sir," Major Davidson now spoke. "They tell us that navy planes from Taffy 3 can chase back that enemy fleet and the navy expects to have more planes from the southern Taffys to help out. They think the Japanese fleet will turn tail as soon as they come under aerial attack, especially after the battering that same enemy fleet took yesterday from the 3rd Fleet carriers."

MacArthur scowled. "Sure, hundreds of planes from a powerful fast carrier fleet: and what happened? The bulk of that fleet still got here. Major, do you think the few planes from the Taffy units, with most of them carrying nothing more than 100 pound anti-personnel bombs, is going to stop that enemy fleet? I'm not putting my faith in the navy anymore, especially with a lamebrain like Halsey in charge. No," he shook his head vigorously, "that Japanese fleet will reach Leyte Gulf and flatten everything on the beaches. I don't want any troops and supplies around when that happens."

"Yes, Sir," Major Davidson said.

MacArthur turned again to Krueger. "Okay, Walt, get on it."

"Yes, Sir," Krueger nodded.

In San Pedro Bay, at the northwest extremity of Leyte Gulf, Admiral Thomas Kinkaid paced the bridge of USS Wasatch, the navy transport that served as flag for his 7th Fleet. Not until 0724 hours, a half hour after the sighting of the 1st Striking Force, did Kinkaid receive word on the approach of the Japanese fleet. His chief aide, Cmdr. James Long, Wasatch ship commander, Captain Al Granum, and other 7th Fleet staff merely watched the obviously distressed Kinkaid. Then, a radio man came onto the bridge.

"Admiral, Sir, a message from Admiral Clifton Sprague."

Kinkaid snapped the slip of paper from the radio man's hand, read, and then pursed his lips. "Taffy 3 has launched planes to hit that Japanese fleet. They got off 50 or 60 bombers and fighters."

"That won't be enough to slow them down," Captain Granum grumbled. "The whole 3rd Fleet couldn't stop them yesterday. What can fifty planes do?"

"Not much," Kinkaid agreed. He then looked at his aide. "What was the last reported position of that enemy task force?"

"About fifty miles northeast of Leyte Gulf, off the coast of Samar."

"That means they'll be in Leyte Gulf in two or three hours, depending on how much Ziggy Sprague can slow them down." Then: "Any word from Admiral Olendorf? What about his battleships and cruisers?"

"He's just turning to, Sir," Cmdr. Long said, "but he's at least two or three hours from Dinagat Island even at full ahead."

"And Halsey's carriers?"

"We've notified Admiral Halsey," Cmdr. Long continued, "but I'm afraid the 3rd Fleet carriers are too far north. They won't even reach aircraft launch range for three hours. I don't think we can depend on Halsey in this thing."

Kinkaid nodded and then sighed. "All right, we'll pull out of Leyte Gulf. Send a message to all ship commanders. They should aweigh at once and sail towards Surigao Strait. Hopefully, we'll run into Olendorf's battleship-cruiser force and the South Attack Force can take it from there."

"But Sir," Long protested, "we've got more than 200 vessels of all kinds here in San Pedro Bay — transports, freighters, LST's, repair ships, everything. I don't know how they can aweigh at the same time without running into each other."

"He's right, Admiral," one of the other staff said. "Maybe there's still a chance. Admiral Sprague is recalling all CAP's and ground support air units. They can refuel and reload on their jeep carriers to make strikes on those Japanese warships. And Admiral Sample expects to mount a hundred planes to hit that same Japanese fleet."

Kinkaid scowled. "You're wishful thinking, Commander. As Captain Granum said, that won't be enough to slow them down. You've heard the reports. Japanese naval guns have already knocked apart CVE Kalinin Bay, and hurt some of the other jeep carriers of Taffy 3. Sprague might not even have carrier decks to retrieve aircraft, much less send them out again after those ships. As for Sample, I don't think his southern Taffy units can mount a hundred planes. He's already sent out most of his aircraft with heavy bombs and torpedoes to hit those surface ship cripples in the Sulu Sea. No," Kinkaid shook his head, "we'll need to get everything we can out of Leyte Gulf."

"What about Admiral Sprague, Sir?" Cmdr. Jim Long asked.

Admiral Kinkaid looked hard at his aide. "He's on his own. Now pass on the order, Commander; aweigh all ships and head for Surigao Strait."

"Yes, Sir," Long answered.

Within the next five minutes almost every GI on Leyte and every bluejacket in San Pedro Bay had heard the orders from General MacArthur and Admiral Kinkaid. For the Army: evacuate inland; for the Navy: set sail south for Surigao Strait.

On the shoreline of Leyte, Army service troops and army air force ground personnel listened with increasing anxiety to the continued approach of the powerful Japanese fleet. The men huddled about radios to hear the intermittent squawk box talk between jeep carriers. The reports were hardly encouraging.

"Enemy fleet closing fast."

"Heavy damage to carrier deck."

"Fires aboard; heavy fires aboard!"

"Battleship shells intense and close."

"Enemy cruisers now estimated at 20,000 yards."

A half hour after the sighting of 1st Striking Force, the soldiers of the 6th Army and 5th Army Air Force were quite convinced that the enemy fleet would enter Leyte Gulf. This sudden change of fortune was shocking, considering the increasing good news since the Leyte invasion five days ago. Until this precarious morning of October 25, these men on shore had seen enemy ground, air, and sea opposition drastically diminish with each passing day. But now, all the fears they had felt during the initial invasion had swelled inside of them again.

Soon, navy men joined the army GI's on shore: sailors from Higgins boats, other small craft, and even beached LST's and LCI's. These bluejackets were also convinced of an impending disaster in Leyte Gulf. When they heard that 6th Army headquarters had ordered an evacuation inland, hundreds of sailors had elected to take their chances with the army rather than attempt to run from San Pedro Bay aboard their ships as ordered by Admiral Thomas Kinkaid. Most of these sailors expected the Japanese fleet to run over Ziggy Sprague's baby flat tops and then come into Leyte Gulf to pulverize any ships in its path. Few sailors believed the 7th Fleet auxiliary non-combat vessels could escape the big 18", 14", and 8" salvos from Japanese battleships and cruisers.

When Admiral Kinkaid heard that hordes of his sailors had joined the army, he shook his head in disappointment. When MacArthur heard the news, he grinned for the first time that morning.

"That proves that these sailors have a lot more sense than their commander," MacArthur told Krueger. "They've got hope with us compared to their chances aboard those scows that try to get out of San Pedro Bay."

Krueger nodded and then looked out of his head-quarters hut at the low, broken clouds that had dumped intermittent rain for the past several hours. "Well, we may not have to worry about air attacks today."

"Japanese planes are the least of our worries," MacArthur answered.

But, General Douglas MacArthur did not realize that an astonishing Japanese air Strategy would come to pass from the Japanese airbases at Mabalacat, outside of Manila, and from Davao on the island of Mindanao.

Admiral Takijiro Onishi, commander of the Japanese 6th Base Air Force at Clark Field, Luzon, had watched with dismay the diminishing fortunes of the Japanese air units during the invasion of the Philippines by the Americans. He had seen U. S. carrier planes paste the Japanese bases on Luzon, Cebu, and Negros with devastating effectiveness during the first weeks of October, while 5th Air Force planes from Morotai had smashed Japanese air bases in Mindanao. Onishi had seen his inexperienced pilots fall prey to superior Corsair and Hellcat pilots who were better trained and more experienced.

Then had come the disastrous air battles in and around Formosa during the third week of October, where Japanese air units had suffered heavy defeats against Admiral Halsey's 3rd U. S. Fleet carrier pilots, and where 3rd Fleet planes had wrecked at least a half dozen Formosa airfields.

The series of misfortunes had prompted Admiral Onishi to reach a disheartening conclusion: Japanese airmen could not stop the Americans by conventional aerial attacks.

After the Formosa air battle defeats, Admiral Onishi had approached Admiral Shigeru Fukudome with a startling proposal. 'Honorable Fukudome, I would make a brazen suggestion. It is my opinion that there is no way to assure success against the enemy with our meagre air strength and inexperienced pilots. I propose that we organize suicide attack units composed of Mitsubishi fighter planes and armed with two 250 kilogram bombs. Each aircraft will crash dive into an enemy aircraft carrier — one aircraft, one enemy carrier."

Admiral Fukudome had expressed shock at the proposal. "You are mad, Takijiro," the 2nd Air Fleet commander had answered. "How can you even suggest that we deliberately sacrifice our young pilots in such a manner? True, the war goes badly, and we have lost many good pilots. But, we have not sent our pilots to certain suicide."

"Admiral," Onishi answered soberly, "only with such tactics can we hope to prevent the Americans from reaching our homeland."

The debate had continued for several hours before Onishi had finally convinced the shocked Fukudome of the merits of suicide planes. In view of the lopsided disasters between Japanese and American air units, Fukudome knew they needed something audacious and he agreed to the formation of suicide units. However, he did not give Onishi permission to use such air units unless the situation became desperate.

Admiral Onishi had then called on the commanders and squadron leaders of his 201st and 761st Air Groups, including Captain Rikihei Inoguchi, Captain Shoichi Sugita, and Lt. Hiroshi Nishizawa, Japan's leading air ace with more than a hundred kills during four years of war. Nishizawa had shot down 20

American planes during the Solomons campaign alone, and several times he had been given up for dead. But still, he listened with the same sober face as did the others when Onishi explained his proposal.

"We must understand that neither ministers nor admirals can any longer save our homeland," Onishi had told his air commanders. "Our nation's salvation lies in the sinking of American aircraft carriers with our young pilots."

After a few moments of silence, Cmdr. Assaichi Tamai, the executive officer of the 201st Air Group, had stepped forward. "We will exert ourselves to the utmost, Honorable Onishi. You may entrust the entire responsibility to the 201st Air Group."

When Onishi looked at the 201st commander, Captain Inoguchi nodded. "Cmdr. Tamai speaks also for me, Admiral. We will initiate such a special attack group at once, as soon as possible."

By October 21, the day after the American invasion of the Philippines, Captain Inoguchi had formed the first special attack units, selecting 24 pilots from a horde of volunteers who had come forward to join this incredible corps, the Shimpu Special Attack Corps.

Captain Rikihei Inoguchi had prepared 24 Zero suicide planes. One squadron, the Yamato Special Attack Force, included 12 aircraft under Lt. Yosunori Aoki. This unit would be based at Davao in Mindanao. The other unit, the Shikishima Special Attack Force under Lt. Yukio Seki, also included 12 planes, and was based in Mabalacat, near Manila. 74 Squadron would provide escort for the Yamato suicide unit out of Davao, and Onishi had designated

83 Squadron under the renowned Hiroshi Nishizawa as escort for the Shikishima unit.

The suicide pilot volunteers had gladly assumed the responsibility to kill themselves if such a death could protect their homeland. They took courage from two famed Samurai poems, the first reflecting the Shikishima Yamato spirit that they hoped to emulate:

"If one were to ask what is the Yamato spirit of
    Japan,
        The reply would be, it is like the fragrant wild
            cherry
    Abloom in the morning sun."

The suicide pilots also took heart from a most famous Samurai poem that gave a philosophy for the highest form of Japanese patriotism:

"If I go away to sea,
    I shall return a corpse awash;
If duty calls me to the mountain,
    A verdant sward will be my pall;
Thus for the sake of the Emperor,
    I shall not die peacefully at home."

On the day after the invasion of Leyte, October, 21, Admiral Onishi had called together the 24 suicide volunteers from both Davao and Mabalacat for one last speech. "I regret that you will be unable to know the results of your sacrificial mission against the enemy fleet. But your escorting wingmen will verify the results to me at once. Then, without fail, I will report your efforts to your departed spirit and to the throne (The Emperor). Therefore, I ask you to resolutely carry out your mission without remorse."

Still, even with the American landings at Leyte,

Admiral Fukudome had not given Onishi permission to use the suicide pilots. But, conditions had soon worsened. The 2nd Striking Force had been almost annihilated in Surigao Strait. 1st Striking Force had taken losses, Ozawa's carrier force had been running from the powerful American 3rd Fleet, U. S. 6th Army troops were pushing inland from the Leyte beaches, American carrier planes were still pasting Fukudome's air bases. And yesterday, October 24, when Fukudome finally sent a massive air unit to Leyte, the effort had totally failed with the loss of 80 Japanese planes to U. S. navy pilots from 3rd Fleet carriers Langley, Essex, and Princeton.

At about 0500 hours, October 25, 1944, Admiral Shigeru Fukudome had received the bad news of the beating taken by Admiral Nishimura's 2nd Striking Force. He now realized that he would probably need to use suicide pilots to stem off further disaster. Fukudome was further encouraged to take such steps when he learned that Kurita's 1st Striking Force had cleared San Bernadino Strait and was sailing towards Leyte Gulf. The 2nd Air Fleet commander must do whatever he could to stop any air attacks on Kurita's fleet from the American Taffy units.

So, however agonizing, Fukudome called Admiral Onishi out of bed. "Takijiro, you may use the special attack forces against the enemy's escort carriers off Samar and south of Leyte Gulf."

"It is the only way, Honorable Fukudome."

Onishi immediately called Davao and authorized the use of the Yamato Special Attack Force against the southern U. S. Taffy groups. Almost at once, before daylight, Lt. Yosunori Aoki had taken off with six suicide planes under escort of six Zeros from Davao's 74 Squadron. By 0600 hours, the Yamato unit was heading for the southern American Taffy units south of Leyte Gulf.

For the remainder of the early morning, Fukudome felt misgivings about sending out suicide planes. Then, at 0700 hours on this same October 25, 1944 morning, Fukudome had learned that Admiral Kurita's fleet had opened fire on the American escort carrier group off Samar. What better way to help Kurita than to send out suicide planes that could destroy these escort carriers?

At 0705 hours, Fukudome again called Admiral Onishi. "Takijiro, you may use the Shikishima Special Attack force against the American carriers off Samar. Aircraft from these escort carriers may otherwise interfere with Kurita's mission."

"Yes, Honorable Fukudome," Onishi answered. The 6th Base Air Force commander then called Captain Rikihei Inoguchi of the 201st Air Group. "You will launch at once the Shikishima Special Attack Force to destroy the American escort carriers off the island of Samar so this force cannot stop Admiral Kurita's advance into Leyte Gulf."

"At once, Admiral," Captain Inoguchi answered.

By 0730 hours, seven suicide pilots of the Shikishima unit had conducted a final ritual, a prayer service, a rededication to the Samurai spirit, and a glass of saki. Then, Lt. Seki and the other Divine Wind pilots prepared for their one way trip to oblivion.

Lt. Hiroshi Nishizawa soberly watched this final formality. The navy pilot veteran had never refused

90

to fight, even against the worst odds: not in the New Guinea campaign, the Solomons, the western Pacific, or here in the Philippines. But, he frowned on the idea of deliberate suicide. Still, he said nothing, for Nishizawa was first and foremost a true servant of Japan and he would do as he was told. Nishizawa would make every effort with his 83 Squadron of fighter pilots to ward off enemy interceptor planes that might interfere with the suicide planes before the Divine Wind pilots dove into their targets.

By this same 0730 hours, in the Philippine Sea off the coast of Samur, the 1st Striking Force continued its wary pursuit of Taffy 3, while the Japanese ships still lobbed 14", 18" and 8" shells after the fleeing baby flat tops. Astonishingly, with all the activity at the 6th Base Air Force in Mabalacat, Admiral Kurita had yet to receive word from Admiral Fukudome's headquarters. Kurita had no idea whatever that Fukudome now planned to help 1st Striking Force with suicide planes.

The 1st Striking Force commander could only continue his cautious pursuit. "Increase speed to 26 knots," he told chief of staff Koyanagi. "You will also order Desron 10 to launch torpedoes as soon as the division is in position. You should also direct Crudiv 7 to make all speed and close range on the enemy carriers."

"Yes, Admiral," Koyanagi answered.

Kurita then scanned the skies, but he saw neither American planes nor aircraft from the 2nd Air Fleet. By the time the 1st Striking Force commander had completed his scan of the skies, Admiral Koyanagi spoke to him.

"Honorable Kurita, both Desron 10 and Crudiv 7

have acknowledged the order to increase speed and they will carry the order out at once."

Kurita nodded and then asked: "You have not yet heard from Admiral Fukudome?"

"No, Admiral," Koyanagi answered. "Apparently, there have been some problems with communications between here and Manila."

"Try to raise them again," Kurita said. "We must have air support."

The 1st Striking Force commander could not guess that 2nd Air Fleet was coming to his aid in a most mind boggling manner—with 13 suicide pilots.

Aboard the jeep carrier Fanshaw Bay, Admiral Clifton Ziggy Sprague clearly saw the approach of the Japanese cruisers and destroyers, Crudiv 7 and Desron 10. He licked his lips nervously as perspiration dampened the forehead of his round face. He searched the broken cloud skies, but saw no planes, for his aircraft had disappeared to the north to attack the enemy fleet. Then, near panic struck Sprague again: no help from either Kinkaid or Halsey for at least three hours, and no real certainty of help from the southern Taffy groups, despite Admiral Bill Sample's assurances. If Ziggy Sprague did not do something else again soon, his jeep carriers would surely go down.

Now, the Taffy commander squinted from the bridge at his zig-zagging DD's and DDE's of Taffy 3's Desron 46. They were finally laying smoke. Then, a desperate idea struck the worry wart American admiral. His tin cans: could these DD's and DDE's break up the Japanese battle formations? Slow the enemy down? Perhaps give Taffy 3 some precious moments of respite? Sprague called Captain Bill Thomas aboard DD Heermann, the flag of U. S. Desron 46.

"Bill," Sprague told the screen commander, "the situation looks bad. You'll need to go after those Japanese cruisers and battleships. Shoot at them, launch torpedoes, do whatever you can to slow them down and wreck their battle order."

"DD's and DDE's against heavy cruisers and battleships, Sir?" Captain Thomas asked in astonishment.

"You've got to slow up those Japanese ships, maybe long enough for help to come from Kinkaid or Halsey."

"Yes Sir," the Desron 46 commander answered.

The Taffy 3 commander scanned the skimming tin cans of Desron 46; his flag destroyer Heermann, destroyer Hoel, and destroyer Johnson, mere 2100 ton tin cans; and the smaller 1500 ton DDE's with mere 4" and 3" guns: Dennis, John Butler, Raymond, and Samuel Roberts. Did Ziggy Sprague expect Captain Bill Thomas to stop four battleships, eight heavy cruisers, two light cruisers, and a bunch of destroyers with seven tin cans?

Desron 46 would be like a few terriers trying to beat back a pack of Great Danes, like an infantry company attempting to stop a tank division, or a few featherweights trying to floor a couple dozen muscular heavyweights. Even David had a better chance against Goliath, because if Taffy 3's Desron 46 had slingshots, 1st Striking Force not only had the big clubs, but plenty of slingshots of their own, big ones, and the Japanese knew how to use them.

Still, at 0732 hours, Captain Bill Thomas picked up his TBS internship radio phone to send out to the tin can commanders of Desron 46 a most astonishing order: "Prepare to attack enemy fleet."

Chapter Six

When Captain Bill Thomas notified his screen escort vessels of Admiral Ziggy Sprague's request, the skippers of the tin cans reacted with a mixture of shock and disbelief. Attack battleships and cruisers with destroyers and destroyer escorts? The admiral was crazy. Still, the officers and crews of the small American ships braced themselves for this impossible task.

After the seven DD's and DDE's of Desron 46 had laid their smoke screen, they began a patrol along a 30 mile shuttle sweep north of the carriers. DD USS Johnson had already scooted towards the Japanese fleet and had already responded to enemy gunfire by lobbing 5" shells at the enemy cruisers. Captain Thomas made no attempt to recall Johnson to form his Desron 46 into torpedo launch position.

As Destroyer Johnson sailed towards Crudiv 7 to fire her salvos little DDE Samuel Roberts had sailed cautiously behind Johnson. So, Thomas did not recall the DDE, either. He merely made official the advance on the Japanese cruiser line by the two tin cans. Then, Bill Thomas himself led DD's Heermann and Hoel, along with DDE's Dennis, Butler, and Raymond after the Japanese battleships and destroyers.

The USS Johnson had been commissioned almost a year ago at Seattle, Washington, on October 27, 1943. Lt. Cmdr. Ernest Cherokee Evans, a full blooded Indian, had assumed command of the new destroyer. He was a barrel chested, ruggedly built man with straight black hair, a big face, and piercing black eyes. His voice rumbled out of his throat with an ominous tone of authority. The new crew of Johnson almost at once called him The Chief—but never to his face.

Evans told his new crew: "This is going to be a fighting ship and I intend to go into harm's way. Anyone who doesn't want to go along had better get off this ship right now."

Most of the 300 man crew were green, with only Evans, gunnery officer Lt. Jim Hagen, grissly chief Jim O'Dorek and a few others with any combat experience.

But, three months after commissioning, the Johnson saw continuous action. The ship had been part of the bombardment units at Kwajalein, Eniwetok, Bougainville, Guam, and Peleliu. In between, Johnson had hunted Japanese submarines and had sunk at least one. USS Johnson had been at battle stations so often, her crew had dubbed the destroyer GQ Johnny.

Remarkably, all during these months of continuous combat, GQ Johnny had not suffered so much as a paint chip from enemy gunfire or a minor wound among its crew. After Peleliu came a lull. On October

24, 1944 at evening mess, Evans told his officers: "Well, boys, in three days GQ Johnny will be a year old. I wouldn't mind a little action to celebrate our first birthday."

The officers had laughed. They could not guess that within the next 12 hours GQ Johnny would be involved in one of the worst David and Goliath fights of the Pacific war.

Crews aboard USS Johnson had been among the first sailors in the Desron 10 screen to spot the Japanese 1st Striking Force as the fleet sailed southward along the coast of Samar. Big, burly torpedo chief Jim O'Gerek, a 20 year navy veteran with a gravel voice, had been on the aft deck of Johnson where he had heard the dull ack-ack fire in the distance and the whine of a plane. The Brooklynite had then scanned the northern horizon with field glasses, freezing in astonishment when he saw the pagoda masts of Japanese battleships in the distance. When he was sure the vessels were Japanese, O'Gerek had picked up a phone and called the bridge.

"Captain," the burly chief had said to Cmdr. Ernie Cherokee Evans, "on the northern horizon, Japanese battleships! Bearing about 170 degrees and about 25 knots. They're off to the southwest."

Evans had screwed his big face, a tinge of anger in his coal black eyes. "O'Gerek, have you been drinkin' torpedo juice again?"

"No Sir, Captain, no sir," the burly torpedo chief had answered sharply. "They're enemy battle wagons."

Evans tightened his grip on the bridge JV phone.

"O'Gerek, if I come back there and find out you've been drinking again, I'll bounce your head on the poopdeck." But, the Cherokee Indian from Charlotte, North Carolina, had barely reprimanded the torpedo chief when he had heard the first echo of naval guns roll across the wide expanse of the Philippine Sea with thundering concussions.

"Jesus, what the hell was that?" Evans asked the bridge officer.

The helmsman shook his head.

Evans called O'Gerek again. "Who's firing, Chief?"

"The battleships have opened up on the CVE's."

"But you said they were 25 knots out."

"They are."

"I felt those concussions shake the bridge."

"That's what 18" shells will do, Sir," O'Gerek answered.

Now, Evans paled. If the Japanese were miles away and the concussions were so intense, the enemy battleships were indeed of the new Yamato class with their 18.1" guns. Cherokee Evans rushed to the port bridge deck and squinted to the north. Now, even with the naked eye, he could see the hazy outlines of pagoda masts. Then, Evans had heard the whine of aircraft—navy Avengers and Hellcats obviously taking off from jeep carriers. He rushed to the port bridge again and then felt another booming vibration as a new broadside of Japanese battleship shells sailed again towards the jeep carriers. He had only time to see the planes racing over his destroyer before a new concussion of heavy shells knocked him against a bulkhead.

Then, before Evans could do anything else, he

had gotten the call from Captain Bill Thomas of Desron 46. "Japanese fleet bearing down on us. Make smoke!"

"Aye aye," Cherokee Evans had answered over the TBS.

A moment later, the whoop alarm echoed throughout the ship as the bridge officer released smoke. Then, Evans had called his gunnery officer, Lt. Bob Hagen. "Get your gun crews ready, Bob, we're laying smoke now and then we may go in for a torpedo and shellfire attack."

"Aye, Sir," Hagen had answered.

Even as Evans spoke the booming 18" shells sailed over the Desron 46 screen, and the seven DD's and DDE's emitted smoke to hide the scurrying jeep carriers. By 0715, when the smoke was laid, Evans had then steered GQ Johnny northward and he had ordered gunnery officer Bob Hagen to open with 5" salvos while chief Jim O'Gerek readied torpedoes. So when the radio man brought the message from Captain Bill Thomas, to attack the Japanese fleet, USS Johnson was already engaging.

Evans merely shrugged at the message, watched a 5" salvo explode short in front of the Japanese Crudiv 7 column, and Cherokee then called the engine room. "Increase speed to 25 knots." He then turned to his helmsman. "Stay on course." Finally, Evans called Lt. Hagen. "A little short, Bob. Raise her."

"Aye aye, Sir."

As Johnson plowed towards the Japanese cruiser column, a little wolf, DDE Samuel Roberts under Lt. Cmdr. Bob Copeland, came right behind the destroyer. The DDE popped 3" shells at the big Japanese cruiser while Lt. Hagen increased fire from Johnson, sending rapid 5" salvos from the DD's main battery at cruiser Kumano. From the bridge of the Crudiv 7 flag, Admiral Shiraishi stared in surprise at the oncoming American tin cans. The small ships were heading directly towards his head cruiser. Shiraishi looked at the Kumano commander, Captain Sasi Hitomo.

"Do my eyes deceive me? Are those two American destroyers coming on to attack our heavy cruiser column?"

"Only one destroyer, Admiral," Captain Hitomo grinned. "The other is a mere destroyer escort with 3" and 4" guns."

"We will use a secondary battery to deal with these brazen vessels," Shiraishi said, "while we continue to attack the American carriers with our main batteries."

"Yes Admiral," Captain Hitomo said.

The two American tin cans, meanwhile, came on, puffing heavily as they slid across the open sea. Then, Evans ordered more smoke as they approached Kumano. But suddenly, Johnson bounced as a salvo of 6" shells landed some 1,000 yards off the starboard bow of the destroyer. Huge colored geysers spewed upwards as the men aboard Johnson hung on. Then, a 14" shell plopped and exploded near Johnson as a Japanese battleship got in a salvo. The concussion threw O'Gerek and the others of the torpedo crew off their feet. Then, the Johnson bluejackets turned and watched more 14" and 18" shells exploding around the zig-zagging baby flat tops that tried desperately to avoid the heavy Japanese shellfire.

On the bridge, Evans turned to his helmsman. "Maintain flank speed."

"Aye, Sir."

As the cruisers of Crudiv 7 continued fire at the little American destroyer, Ernie Evans never faltered. He drove GQ Johnny on. Evans had been in unequal fights before: against a Japanese cruiser at Bougainville, a battleship at Guam, a Japanese carrier at Peleliu. But, Evans had never before attempted to take on a battleship-cruiser fleet with a mere little wolf DE for support. Johnson continued her run across the choppy sea, north, cutting a hugh wash on both sides of her prow. Her twin stacks plumed thick, heavy smoke. Her torpedo crews stood on the ready.

"Prepare for torpedo launch!" Evans cried from the bridge JV.

The bluejackets aboard Johnson tightened their lifejackets, adjusted their helmets, and readied torpedoes, as the U. S. destroyer plowed towards the enemy cruisers. In fact, an almost strange calm prevailed among Chief Jim O'Gerek and his torpedo crew on this potentially fatal fight.

Uncannily, as the Japanese cruisers continued to send 6" salvos at Johnson, not a single shell hit, although some near misses numbed the Johnson crewmen with concussions. Finally, the grizzly O'Gerek barked sharply. "Launch torpedoes!"

At a 25 knot speed, Johnson had closed to 10,000 yards on Kumano when O'Gerek released a spread of five torpedoes. The torpedoes ran hot and straight and a few minutes later, an explosion rocked Kumano and obscured the port midsection of the heavy cruiser.

"We got the bastard, we got her!" O'Gerek cried gleefully.

O'Gerek didn't know it, but a torpedo had hit and smashed Kumano's bow. Then, seconds later, another explosion shuddered Kumano. The new hit ripped a hole in the forward deck of the Japanese cruiser, knocked out a gun turret, and put the Japanese warship into a slight list. Repair crews worked furiously to stop the leaks, pumping out water to right Kumano. The hits from GQ Johnny had forced the Kumano crew to break off its attack on both Johnson and the Taffy 3 carriers.

The Japanese were furious and 14" guns of Battleship Nagata now joined Crudiv 7 in the attack on Johnson. A 14" shell hit GQ Johnny's forecastle, chopping a gaping hole and lifting several shrapnel ridden sailors skyward before dumping their bodies into the sea. Corpsmen rushed frantically to treat another dozen wounded.

"Maintain 30 degree course; I'm going to check casualties," Evans told the helmsman. Then, as Evans left the bridge house and started towards the forecastle area, an enemy shell struck Johnson's port side and threw Evans halfway across the deck. Evans rose to his feet and woozily returned to the bridge.

"Captain," the bridge officer said, "they knocked out the fire room and cut a 10 yarder in the hull."

Evans nodded and then cowered with the bridge staff as another 8" shell, probably from Chikuma, the second ship in the Crudiv 7 line, struck the starboard quarter of Johnson. The explosion sent shrapnel and metal fragments skyward and slammed Evans into a bulkhead, where he bounced off and fell to the deck.

The bridge officer lifted Evans to his feet. "Are you all right, Sir? You okay? Maybe I'd better call a corpsman."

"I'm okay, okay," Evans waved him off while he wiped blood from his arm. He then rushed to the JV room. "Damage control, what's the damage?"

"One of the engine rooms is out, Sir. We've slowed to 15 knots. Fire crews are working hard to stem fires."

Evans tried to concentrate. He closed his eyes and brushed a hand across his furrowed brow. "Okay, we'll have to get out of here," he told the helmsman. "Hard to, 120 degrees."

As GQ Johnny veered to retire, the crew cringed from more 8" shells that churned exploding geysers all around the little destroyer. Still, the U. S. sailors saw the smoke rising from the listing Kumano as the flag of Crudiv 7 veered out of line. And in fact, because of the damage to Kumano, Admiral Kuzutaka Shiraishi decided to shift his flag to the cruiser Suzuya.

But, as Johnson retired, at 0740 hours, the destroyer took more hits. Three 14" shells from a battleship, followed by three 6" hits from a light cruiser, probably Yahagi, smacked into the little destroyer like a truck smashing into a puppy dog. Shells knocked out Johnson's gyro compass, finished the #1 engine room, wrecked steering, and wrecked power.

The destroyer slowed to 17 knots. Then came another 6" hit that snapped clean the mast, tumbling the SC radar down to the bridge and killing three officers. Then, another 14" opened a hole in the deck, the blast killing a dozen bluejackets. The hit also penetrated the bridge, blowing off Cmdr. Evans' clothing from the waist up and chopping off two of Evans' fingers.

However, Evans did not stop. He cried into his JV. "Control! Control!"

All stations answered positive to control testing as repair crews shifted to manual steering and repaired the FD radar in a few minutes. Then, a rain squall swept over Johnson, giving her a valuable ten minute respite and allowing the injured Evans to assess damage. Repair crews had restored enough power to Number 3 and Number 5 guns for partial fire control. Gun crews could at least shift to match pointers by hand, sight manually, and still fire their guns. The gunners of GQ Johnny thus spewed another salvo of 5" shells at the Japanese cruiser column before she hid in the rain squall and in her own smoke.

Some 3,000 yards behind Johnson, and while Johnson temporarily retired from the lopsided fight against Crudiv 7 and apparently Desron 10, Lt. Cmdr. Bob Copeland led his DE Samuel Roberts towards the cruiser column. Obscured by the rain squall and smoke that had given Johnson a temporary respite, Copeland had driven his DE within 4,000 yards of Crudiv 7 without detection. When Samuel Roberts came into the open and saw the big cruisers loom before it, Lt. Cmdr. Copeland cried into his JV.

103

"Launch torpedos! And commence fire with forward turrets!"

Copeland's torpedo crew responded and sent a spread of three torpedoes after the second ship in the Japanese column, Chikuma. The fish ran hot and normal, but the Chikuma helmsman successfully avoided. However, the 4" gun salvo straddled Chikuma and knocked out a storage locker and a 40MM gun pit. The hits enraged the cruiser commander and he trained his 8' main battery on little Samuel Roberts. A heavy salvo barely fell short and almost jerked the DDE out of the water. Copeland turned frantically to his helmsman.

"Let's get the hell out of here. Let's move—and make smoke."

"Aye, Sir," the helmsman said as he quickly spun the wheel hard. The little Samuel Roberts almost listed 30 degrees in its sharp 180 degree turn, sending up a water geyser almost 50 feet high. Only a few minutes later, Samuel Roberts was again on the tail of Johnson, this time retiring.

The next ship in the Desron 46 unit, DDE Raymond did not follow after DD's Heermann, Hoel, and DDE Dennis and DDE John Butler. Raymond lost sight of these four ships and her skipper, Lt. Cmdr. Al Byer, turned his DDE due north, plowed completely past the rest of the Desron 46 ships and reached the two heavy cruisers of Crudiv 5, Haguro and Chokai. When the big enemy ships loomed in front of him, Byer did not hesitate.

"Launch torpedoes! Launch torpedoes!" he cried into his JV.

However, before torpedo crews could act, cruiser

104

Haguro promptly turned her forward 8" guns on the American tin can and unloosened a salvo that landed some 200 to 300 yards astern of the speeding DE and almost raised Raymond's fantail out of the water with the concussions. Haguro would eventually send 15 salvos against the spunky DDE.

Byer again ordered a torpedo launch. However, before the crew could respond, Cruiser Haguro sent a torpedo spread of its own. The sailors aboard Raymond gaped in awe as they saw the four wakes skimming through the water past their DE, the nearest one only 20 yards off the port bow. But, the American sailors recovered quickly and sent off their own three torpedo spread from a distance of a mere 6,000 yards. The heavy cruiser Haguro was at the moment turning to get into position for another torpedo launch against the brazen American DDE. So, unfortunately for Raymond, her torpedoes missed, with two torpedoes passing the stern of Haguro.

The Haguro captain reddened, incensed by the brazen attempt to torpedo his ship. He immediately sent a new salvo of 8" shells that erupted colored geysers in an erratic display of beautiful splashes behind the zig-zagging Raymond. Still, the spunky American DDE refused to give in.

"90 degree left, 90 degree left, and commence fire," Al Byer cried.

"Aye, Sir."

The destroyer escort scudded full right and a moment later, Raymond's gunners loosened a barrage of 3" and 4" shells from her turrets, even as 8" shells from Crudiv 5 straddled the DE, knocking

105

out chunks of her foredeck, a wardroom, a catwalk, and an antiaircraft gun pit. Still, Raymond's gunners fired furiously, expending a fantastic 414 rounds. The Americans scored several hits on huge cruiser Haguro as well as cruiser Chokai and the Crudiv 5 warships veered left and right, to east and to west, so they were at least temporarily distracted from their job of blasting the American jeep carriers.

With all torpedoes expended, all four inch shells gone, and most of the three inch shells used up, Lt. Cmdr. Al Byer ordered a turn about, with a trail of smoke behind him to cover his DDE before the big Japanese ships blew the little wolf out of the water.

The helmsman of Raymond spun into an almost 180 degree turn as engine rooms opened to full ahead. Raymond, zigging and zagging, barely escaped a new salvo of 8" shells from both Chokai and Haguro before the little wolf disappeared behind a pall of her own smoke.

"Bakarya!" the Chokai commander cursed. "She has escaped us. Call Haguro's captain and tell him to come about so we can reform tandem column, and we can then continue the pursuit of the Yankee carriers."

The other tin cans of Desron 46, astonishingly, skimmed right towards the Japanese battleships. Aboard DD Hoel, Cmdr. Larry Kintberger, like other commanders of Desron 46, had reeled from the order to attack the Japanese fleet. Kintberger's helmsman, Ron Barrett, and the bridge officer, Lt. Maury Green, stood in stiff apprehension as they watched Hoel plow towards the enemy capital ships.

"I can't understand this, Sir," Green said to Kintberger, "how the hell could a Japanese fleet sneak up on us like that?"

The Hoel commander shook his head. "A foul up, a lousy foul up."

Lt. Green nodded, but he did not answer. He merely watched their destroyer close towards battleship Kongo, now about 7½ miles to the northeast. When the range closed to 14,000 yards, he looked at Kingberger. "Well?"

Kintberger nodded. Then, at 0743, the Hoel commander ordered Hoel's forward gunners to open on the big battleship. By the time the destroyer loosened four salvos, all of which fell short, Hoel got back a 14" hit from Kongo that struck the bridge and destroyed all radio communication and the radar RPI. The shell also killed several sailors, including Helmsman Barrett who caught a patch of flying shrapnel. Amazingly, Captain Kintberger and Lt. Green only suffered minor cuts.

Commander Kintberger wobbled to the wheel in the battered wheelhouse and spun the destroyer into a 20 degree turn. But, one minute later, another 14" hit struck Hoel's main battery director and killed the antiaircraft officer along with several bluejackets.

"Launch torpedoes! Launch torpedoes!" Cmdr. Kintberger cried into his JV.

The torpedo crew responded and sent off two spreads of three each. One spread passed the battleship Kongo, missing. The other spread fished towards Haguro, the cruiser of Crudiv 2, but these torpedoes also missed. Still, the torpedo combs forced both ships to alter course.

By 0744, the U. S. destroyer Hoel started taking heavy hits. One shell blew the 3" torpedo mount apart, killing the chief torpedo mate and several others. A 14" shell knocked out the port engine room and jammed the rudder, locking the destroyer on a straight heading towards Kongo, an unhealthy course to say the least. Another hit, an 8 incher from Haguro, knocked out JV communications. Still, miraculously, Lt. Glen Coleman, the #1 torpedo mount officer, launched another spread of three torpedoes manually from within 5,000 yards of Haguro. Two missed, but one torpedo caught the Japanese cruiser on the starboard forward and shuddered the big ship to a near stop, slowing her to 20 knots, at least temporarily.

"We've used up torpedoes," Lt. Coleman told Kintberger.

"Then let's get the hell out of here," the Hoel commander answered.

But, Hoel could only turn slightly and nearly ten minutes passed, to 0745 hours, before the destroyer turned herself and limped southwestward. Hoel also made smoke as more 14" and 8" shells from the Japanese ships followed the American destroyer's wake.

Destroyer Heermann had been on Hoel's tail. When Heermann's skipper, Cmdr. Amos Hathaway, saw Hoel launch torpedoes, the Heermann commander launched torpedoes of his own at the Japanese Batdiv 3 and Crudiv 2 columns. Most of Heermann's torpedoes missed, but one struck Kongo in the stern, opening a hole that slowed down the battleship until her repair crews sealed the flooding.

After the strike on Kongo, Cmdr. Amos Hathaway turned to the Desron 46 commander, Captain Bill Thomas. "We got a hit, Captain."

"Pour shells on her," Thomas said eagerly.

Hathaway nodded and called his gunnery officer. "Commence fire on that battleship with forward guns.

"Aye, Sir."

Heermann had only fired one salvo when bridge officer Walter Meadors, peering through his binoculars, gaped in astonishment. Heermann had come within 4,000 yards of Kongo, with battleships Yamato and Nagata off the port bow. Then, off starboard, loomed the slightly damaged Haguro. "My God, Amos, my God," Meadors cried to Cmdr. Hathaway.

Both Heermann's commander and Captain Bill Thomas looked about the sea and found their Heermann in the position of a wounded fox suddenly surrounded by eager hounds. Hathaway ordered a quick course change of 270 degrees for a new torpedo launch. Hathaway also ordered his 5" guns shifted to the huge Yamato. But, as Heermann sent the first 5" salvo after the battleship, Yamato's gunners responded with a salvo of 18" shells that missed but nearly bounced the American destroyer out of the sea. Still, the destroyer's helmsman deftly maneuvered the nimble ship to avoid anything more than near misses. At 746, after flitting about the sea for several minutes to avoid the salvos of heavy shellfire, Heermann launched three more torpedoes at Kongo on a 350 degree track from a mere 4,400 yards.

"That's it," Cmdr. Al Hathaway cried to the helmsman. "Let's get the hell out of here."

The helmsman spun the wheel 100 degrees while engine room opened speed to 26 knots. The destroyer then fled southward while gunners sent salvos of 5" shells at the big Japanese capital ships. The torpedoes and shelling had prompted both Haguro and Yamato to alter course, with Haguro steering north by northeast for almost ten minutes before losing the torpedo tracks.

"Unfortunate, unfortunate," Admiral Koyanagi told Admiral Kurita, "Our ships are scattered again."

"But we must not lose our determination," Kurita answered. "Order Kongo and Haguro to reverse course and increase speed towards the American carriers."

"Yes, Honorable Kurita," Admiral Koyanagi answered.

Heermann, meanwhile, increased speed to a full 35 knots and she safely escaped the big battleships, amazingly, without any damage.

Small Dennis had gone after cruiser Chokai of Crudiv 2. At 0735, she opened with her 4" guns, but a return salvo of 8" shells straddled her. Two near misses on the port side almost capsized her and she retired quickly, hoping to come back later under a smoke screen. DDE John Butler tried to break up the Desron 10 destroyer column. But, Butler had no sooner fired a salvo of 4" shells when a sea full of torpedoes came her way. The little DDE helmsman wheeled Butler frantically almost catpawing over the surface of the sea in deft twists

110

and turns to avoid a torpedo launch from Desron 10.

Then came a rain of 5" shellfire from the same Japanese destroyers that spewed up countless geysers around little John Butler, but not striking the DDE. The Butler commander was simply too exposed and too outgunned, so he retired quickly on the heels of USS Dennis.

The tin can action attack lasted under ten minutes and had caused little damage to the Japanese fleet except for Johnson's hit on Kumano. In return, DD's Johnson and Hoel along with DDE Raymond had been hit quite badly.

But, the Desron 46 assault had accomplished a purpose. The destroyers of Desron 10 were again out of column; Crudiv 7 had scattered, its four ships going off in different directions. The big battleships were all out of position, with at least one of them scooting completely out of the fight temporarily. Crudiv 2's Chokai and Haguro were miles apart from each other.

Admiral Takeo Kurita would need to reform again and come back into range if he hoped to continue his heavy surface ship assault on Taffy 3's carriers.

Chapter Seven

Worry wart Ziggy Sprague took full advantage of the efforts by his small ships of Taffy 3, along with the rain squall that had saved at least two of the Desron 46 vessels from destruction. He put his jeep carriers on a new course, south by south-west, hoping to bring Taffy 3 closer to the hoped for help from the 7th Fleet South Attack Force that was now steaming hard back towards Leyte Gulf. Sprague also hoped to lose the Japanese in the smoke screen and rain squall. As he changed course to the westward, the Taffy 3 commander hoped the Japanese would pursue south to the eastward, where they had last seen the escort carriers.

And true enough, when the rain squall ended and the smoke screens thinned, leaving the sea clear again, the Japanese destroyers of Desron 10 and the cruisers of Crudiv 7 were sailing south by southeast towards the still lingering smoke screen mist. They did not know that Ziggy Sprague had changed course.

From the bridge of the Desron 10 flag, light

cruiser Yahagi, Admiral Susumu Kimura peered irritably through binoculars into the smoke that lay across the surface of the sea. He had about come within range of the escort carriers for his torpedo launch when the pesky Taffy 3 tin cans and the rain squall had abruptly obscured the baby flat tops. Kimura now turned to his gunnery officer, Lt. Cmdr. Tadasi Otani.

"Can you get a bearing on those carriers, Commander?"

"We are trying, Honorable Kimura, but the smoke screens laid by the enemy destroyers still hide the enemy carriers because the air is heavy with humidity and the smoke clings to the sea."

"We must destroy the carriers; we must," Kimura ranted.

"I'm sure we are closing range, Honorable Kimura," Lt. Cmdr. Otani said. "The enemy carriers are surely to the south, southwest of the smoke screen. I see no reason why we should not be in point blank range within an hour."

"If we could only get a glimpse of their position," Kimura said. "What about our search planes? Have they sent a report yet?"

"No, Admiral," the gunnery officer said.

Kimura sighed, disappointed. He would need to wait until the smoke cleared to see the CVE carriers. Or, he would need to wait until a float plane from 1st Striking Force or a reconn plane from 2nd Air Fleet pinpointed the location of the American carriers.

Meanwhile, aboard the Japanese cruiser Kumano, Admiral Kazutaka Shiraishi cursed the damage to

113

his Crudiv 7 flagship. He had come within a few minutes of perhaps finishing off Kalinin Bay and had then been thwarted first by the rain squall and then by the pesky USS Johnson whose torpedo had wrecked the cruiser's bow and slowed her to under 20 knots. Now, Shiraishi decided to shift his flag to cruiser Suzuya.

"You will follow in the rear with Kumano," Shiraishi told the cruiser commander, Captain Sasi Hitomo.

"I will do so," Captain Hitomo answered.

Then, the Kumano sailors helped Admiral Shiraishi and his staff into a motor launch with all Crudiv 7 papers before carrying the staff to the heavy cruiser Suzuya that now came to the head of the column.

Aboard battleship Yamato, Admiral Takeo Kurita also peered through binoculars and glowered at the length of smoke across the horizon. Battleships Yamato, Kongo, and Haruna had been pummelling the jeep carrier fleet with 18" and 14" shells and Kurita was anxious to close for a point blank fire on the American ships. But now, the baby flat tops were lost somewhere behind the smoke screen and he had to reform his own fleet into proper Number 19 battle formation again because of the pesky American Desron 46. The unexpected suspension of shellfire and pursuit had given the Americans another respite.

Now, during this lull, Admiral Kurita found time to mull over the situation and the more he pondered the more he worried. He had no idea what prevailed behind the smoke screen. Were these

114

American flat tops big, fast Independence class American carriers? Were surface ships indeed of the Baltimore heavy cruiser class in the area as well as these DD's and DDE's that had attacked his fleet? And where were the reported American battleships? Were they now steaming northward to enter the fray? Kurita's float planes had not sent back a report, and Kurita guessed that American fighter planes had probably shot them down before the Japanese crews could see the American fleet and radio a report.

Kurita's imagined fears now tempered his enthusiasm. The 1st Striking Force commander turned to Admiral Koyanagi. "We will reduce speed to 15 knots and move cautiously while we reform into battle formation."

"But Admiral," Koyanagi said, "surely, we should give the enemy no respite."

"We are sailing blindly and wasting precious fuel and ammunition," Kurita said. "We must be certain of our targets. We must know their position, and we must be sure that no heavy American vessels, including perhaps battleships, are among the enemy carriers." He pursed his lips. "Reduce speed to 15 knots."

"Yes Admiral," his chief of staff answered.

So, the powerful 1st Striking Force slowed down and ceased firing, except for some sporadic salvos from an occasional Japanese cruiser or destroyer. Still, the temporary suspension of action did give Kurita time to organize his fleet into proper attack disposition before continuing the chase of the American aircraft carriers. Kurita called for battleships

115

Kongo and Haruna to form their tandem column with Desron 2 as screen. He also ordered Desron 10 to move ahead with light cruiser Yahagi and seven destroyers in a torpedo launch formation, a position that Admiral Kimura had pretty well established, before the rain squall and the tin cans of Desron 46 had broken it up.

Admiral Kurita also called Admiral Kazutaka Shiraishi of Crudiv 7. "Kazutaka, it appears we were too rash on this first assault on the enemy carriers. I would ask that you form your cruisers in proper columnar formation to get maximum fire power from your vessels."

"Honorable Kurita," Shiraishi said, "we were doing well until that rain squall and the pesky American destroyers disrupted us. We would have surely sunk an enemy carrier. Unfortunately, cruiser Kumano has been quite damaged and now sails at reduced speed. I have therefore transferred the Crudiv 7 flag to Suzuya." He paused. "You must forgive me, Admiral, if I question your order to reduce speed to 15 knots and to cease fire. Surely, this will give the enemy time to open range."

"Some of my staff agree with you," Kurita said. "Nonetheless, we are at this moment uncertain of our target and during our reduced speed we will have time to reform in Number 19 battle order. Further, we must mark time until we have a clear view of the enemy's position and complement. As soon as I have more information, I will ask your Crudiv 7, Desron 10, and Admiral Kobe's Batdiv 3 to again increase speed."

"Have you scout planes not reported?" Shiraishi asked.

"No," Kurita answered. "I fear the aircraft were lost before the crew could send us a report."

"Then perhaps we can launch another spotter plane."

"I have ordered a new float plane aloft," Kurita said, "but I have done so with misgivings. Enemy fighter planes may shoot down or drive off this new search aircraft. Perhaps we must wait for a reconnaisance report from the 2nd Air Fleet, whose Mitsubishi fighter planes can deal with enemy aircraft while they observe the complement, location, and course of the enemy fleet."

"Perhaps," Admiral Shiraishi said.

By 0740 hours, little less than an hour after the shooting started, the Taffy 3 carriers had made 20 miles in their retreat from the 1st Striking Force. The Japanese fleet, by slowing down, had fallen some 16 to 18 miles behind the American jeep carriers. However, at 0747, the smoke screen finally thinned enough for observers in the Japanese crows nests to again spot Taffy 3. But, the carriers were far from their expected position.

An observer called the bridge of Yamato. "The enemy carriers have moved to the southwest. We estimate their position at 11.45 degrees north and 126.11 degrees west. They are perhaps 30,000 yards from Desron 10 and the enemy makes about 15 knots on a course bearing of 119 degrees."

Kurita scowled. "The enemy has altered its course and now sails towards Leyte Gulf," he told his staff. The 1st Striking Force commander could

117

have altered his own course to a diagonal 140 degrees and perhaps closed to 15,000 or 20,000 yards had he known that Sprague had radically changed course. But, Kurita did not waste time in deploring his missed opportunity. He turned to his aide.

"We will resume flank speed of 30 knots," Kurita told Koyanagi, "and we will order Admiral Kimura to increase his own Desron 10 speed to 32 knots so he may launch torpedoes as soon as he comes within proper range. We will also order Admiral Shiraishi of Crudiv 7 to increase speed to 32 knots so that he can resume fire with his heavy cruisers."

"Yes Admiral," Koyanagi answered.

"Meanwhile, we too shall resume fire, for even from 30,000 yards the big guns of our battleships can strike with telling accuracy."

"Yes, Honorable Kurita," Koyanagi said again.

Almost immediately, the big 18" and 14" guns of 1st Striking Force once more boomed across the Philippine Sea, shuddering the very surface of the water. Once more, huge colored geysers —blue, orange, red, or purple from four Japanese battleships—erupted around the jeep carriers. The battleships were not quite close enough to hit accurately, but within the next 15 or 20 minutes, Kurita would no doubt close enough range to start scoring deadly hits. And worse, the cruisers of Crudiv 7 and the destroyers of Desron 10 were making full flank speed again.

But, as the efforts of Desron 46 had given the imperiled American jeep carriers a respite, now the American aircraft from Taffy 3 would give the carriers a breather.

At the same 0747 hours, as soon as the 1st Striking Force battleships resumed fire, aircraft from the various jeep carriers arrived over the 1st Striking Force complement of vessels.

Cmdr. Bill Keighley, taking his 8 Avengers and 10 Hellcats back to help Kalinin Bay, now roared over the Crudiv 7 column that he had spotted through a hole in the clouds. The Japanese cruisers, at apparent full speed, were jockeying into position to resume fire on the carriers.

Keighley called into his radio. "This is Catnip Leader; now hear this. 2nd Flight leader will take your four planes and attack the lead cruiser in column. Our own 1st Flight will attack the second vessel in column."

"Okay, Bill," the 2nd Flight leader answered.

Keighley then called Lt. Pat Capano and told him to attack the third and fourth cruisers in line. Perhaps the fighter planes could at least disrupt the enemy attack by forcing the cruisers to take evasive action. Keighley knew they could not do much damage against heavy cruisers with 100 pound bombs and 5" rockets and strafing fire. But, if they rattled the column badly enough and if they caused enough damage, the Japanese sailors would need to concentrate on repairs instead of the American jeep carriers.

The Composite Squadron 3 commander hoped that his two Avengers carrying torpedoes would do some real damage.

When Bill Keighley came within a mile of cruiser Tone, an eruption of ack-ack fire blackened the sky. Still, Keighley ignored the exploding black puffs

119

and dove from 8,000 feet down to 500 feet before roaring towards cruiser Tone, with two other Avengers of his lead flight a thousand yards behind him at the same 500 feet altitude. The Squadron 3 commander roared over zig-zagging Tone and unleashed his six centuries (100 pound bombs). The explosions straddled the stern of the Japanese ship in a series of hits that exploded in a staccato of bursts from star board to aft of midship on the port side. Three of the bombs scored direct hits, one fell short, and the others sailed beyond the target to explode in the water. The next plane in this lead flight unleashed a half dozen centuries too and this Avenger also scored hits, although most of the bombs missed.

However, the third aircraft in this first flight caught an ack-ack hit just under the belly and the torpedo bomber burst into fragments of metal and fire before the plane and its three man crew splashed into the sea.

2nd Flight now roared towards the lead cruiser Suzuya where Kimura had transferred his flag. As the helmsman spun the wheel, the cruiser sent up heavy sprays of sea water from the aft that almost washed over the stern of the ship. But, the quick maneuver enabled Suzuya to avoid any serious damage, especially since two of the Catnip Avengers carried torpedoes. Most of the hundred pounders from 2nd Flight landed far short and erupted harmless geysers in the sea. Two of the small bombs did hit the aft section, ripping away a piece of deck, damaging a bulkhead, and killing four Japanese sailors. The torpedoes, however, skimmed harmlessly past the stern of Suzuya, bringing disappointment to Bill Keighley. Again, the attack had been costly as ack-ack fire blew another Avenger out of the sky, with the fragments of the plane and crew dropping into the sea.

The ten Hellcats from Keighley's Squadron 3 made similar three plane runs over the other two cruisers of Crudiv 7, Chikuma and limping Kumano. Heavy ack-ack fire threw up a wall of exploding black puffs at the approaching American fighter planes. The ten Hellcats sprayed the cruiser decks with .50 caliber fire. However, except for a half dozen dead and dozen wounded, the Hellcat attack had caused no damage to Chikuma or Kumano, only consternation among their crews. And, once more, the Japanese antiaircraft gunners took a toll. The cruisers' ack-ack crews knocked two of the attacking Hellcats out of the sky.

When Bill Keighley reformed his planes after the strike on Crudiv 7, he cursed in frustration. He had lost four planes and he had barely put a dent in the heavy cruisers. He could only hurry back to his carrier, Kalinin Bay, to reload and try again. Keighley did not know that Japanese cruiser shells had punched his Kalinin Bay deck full of holes. In fact, he did not know that only through the Grace of God, with the sudden rain squall, was Kalinin Bay still afloat.

Still, despite his disappointment, Bill Keighley had given Admiral Sprague and his jeep carrier commanders another pause. The aerial attack by the eight Avengers and ten Hellcats had not hurt the cruisers, but the attack had once more thrown the cruisers out of their battle formation and Crudiv 7 needed to reorganize still again before resuming their 8" shelling on the American jeep carriers.

Commander Bob Fowler of Kitkun Bay had rendezvoused his 16 Avengers and 12 Hellcats at 0730 hours. At the same 0747 hours, he was leading his aircraft against light cruiser Yahagi and the seven destroyers of Desron 10 that were closing on Taffy 3 from the northeast to launch torpedoes. Cmdr. Fowler and his wingman, Lt. Walter Crocker, had been droning northward at 8,000 feet above a totally overcast sky when Fowler picked up blips on his aircraft radar – ships just eight miles ahead. And soon, ack-ack fire spewed up the approaching planes. Fowler immediately led his 16 Avengers and 12 Hellcats down to 1500 feet, under the clouds, and through the ack-ack fire. The Composite Squadron 5 immediately scattered in pairs to avoid hits from the antiaircraft fire.

"We've got eight ships down there," Cmdr. Fowler cried into his TBS. "Let's pick our targets. Crocker and I will go after the cruiser. The rest of you, in pairs, go after those destroyers."

A moment later, 600 yards apart, Fowler and Crocker dropped to 500 feet and zoomed towards Yahagi that now zigged and zagged while her antiaircraft gunners rattled 20MM and 40MM pom pom fire at the approaching planes – torpedo bombers that only carried 100 pound bombs and 5" fire rockets instead of torpedoes.

The low sky under the clouds became so thick with black puffs of flak that Fowler and his wingman barely saw the cruiser. Still, they roared on.

Then, Fowler dropped his 100 pound bombs and unleashed a stream of rockets from his 5" tubes. But, only one bomb hit, knocking out a small machine gun pit. The other bombs fell on either side of the cruiser while the rockets fell short, spewing blobs of sea water behind Yahagi's stern. Fowler barely arched away to avoid ack-ack hits.

Now came Lt. Crocker, also zooming over target at 500 feet before he too unleashed a stream of rockets and a half dozen 100 pounders. But, nothing from the plane hit as Yahagi's helmsman effectively maneuvered his light cruiser to avoid both the bombs and rockets. Lt. Crocker scowled in disappointment. If he had only had heavy bombs or torpedoes. And worse, from the corner of his eye, he could see the disaster that befell two Avengers of Composite Squadron 5 that were attacking destroyer Nowaki to his right. Crocker saw one of the bombers get hit by a barrage of ack-ack fire that cut the plane in half before crew and plane fragments plopped into the sea. And, before Crocker came out of his dive, he saw a second Avenger trail heavy smoke, wobble for nearly a mile, try to gain altitude, and finally plop fatally into the sea. The Japanese gunners had downed two American planes before the aircraft had even released bombs or rockets on the zig zagging Desron 10 destroyer.

On the deck of Nowaki, the Japanese gunners cheered, while on the bridge, both Captain Tone Tanii and his bridge officer, Lt. Cmdr. Hasi Nakamura, exchanged grins. They had downed two enemy planes without catching a single hit. But then, they suddenly cowered as rattling strafing fire from a trio of Hellcats raked the main and upper decks with .50 caliber fire. However, the tracers had only shaken the Japanese sailors, but had not caused any deaths, injuries, or damage. For its trouble, Composite Squadron 5 lost two Hellcats.

The rest of Squadron 5 fared the same—frustration in their attempt to hit the other destroyers of Desron 10. Pairs of Avengers went after the destroyers Urakaze, Hamakaze, Isokaze, Kiyoshimo, Yukakaze, and Fujinami. But, the Japanese helmsmen adeptly maneuvered their vessels to avoid serious harm, while ack-ack fire effectively threw off the aim of the diving Avengers. The destroyers suffered only a few hundred pound hits and perhaps a dozen rocket hits, none of which caused serious damage, although one of the rockets knocked out a 40MM antiaircraft pit aboard Yukakaze and killed the gun crew.

The Composite Squadron 5 attack on Desron 10 had been a near total failure in terms of damage, but Cmdr. Fowler and his crews and pilots had again thrown a formation of Japanese surface ships out of battle formation. Admiral Kimura's ships had been forced to scatter in the face of the Avenger and Hellcat attacks. They would need to reorganize and make up lost time before launching torpedoes at the American jeep carriers.

Perhaps Cmdr. Ed Huxtable of Gambier Bay attempted the most daring attack of the early morning. He led his nine Dauntlesses and twelve Hellcats against the big battleships of Batdiv 1, Nagata and Yamato with their 18" guns. Even before he approached the battleships, Huxtable guessed that his task was impossible. An array of countless guns stuck out of every part of these ships like porcupine quills. A barrage of ack-ack fire practically blotted out the two battleships and the flight through the ack-ack puffs was like running through a fatal gauntlet. Still, Huxtable did not hesitate. He could not because one solid 14" or 18" hit on a jeep carrier could blow the baby flat top out of the water.

"This is Dexter Leader," Huxtable called into his TBS. "1st Flight Dauntlesses will follow me and 1st Flight Hellcats will come in after us to strafe decks. 2nd Flight bombers will take on the tandem battleship and 2nd Flight flighters will strafe decks of tandem battleship."

"Roger," Lt. Bob Roby of the Avenger 2nd Flight said.

Huxtable now led his flight of five Dauntlesses into the mouth of Yamato's big guns. From the bridge of the huge dreadnought, Admiral Kurita, Admiral Ugaki, and Admiral Koyanagi looked on in awe—not at the aircraft attack, but at the audacity of five Dauntlesses to attack this ship in the face of so many guns.

"They are reckless, utterly reckless," Admiral Ugaki said. "How can they expect to meet anything but death with so few light bombers?"

"They have courage," Admiral Kurita answered soberly, "and they will need every ounce of such courage if they expect to survive an attack on this vessel."

So confident were the staff of 1st Striking Force on Yamato's bridge that they did not even seek cover.

And, despite the huge target offered by Yamato, Admiral Kurita was correct. Before the five Dauntlesses reached the battleship, ack-ack gunners had blown two of the American dive bombers out of the sky. The other Dauntless pilots, including Huxtable, quickly arched away from the heavy ack-ack fire to avoid the same fate. However, the three Dauntlesses then circled back and came in on the starboard quarter to unleash their bombs and rockets. But, the intense ack-ack fire had prompted Huxtable and the others to release their bombs and rockets a little too soon. The rockets splashed and exploded harmlessly into the sea as did most of the century bombs. A pair of hundred pounders did hit and explode, but the explosions merely clanged off the thick plating of Yamato.

Equally useless were the strafing runs by Hellcats of Composite Squadron 10. The stream of .50 caliber fire prompted Japanese sailors to cower behind strong metal platings where they winced from strafing bullets that pinged off the plates. For the futile efforts by the Hellcats, they lost two fighter planes from the heavy antiaircraft fire. One plane exploded in mid air. The other, hit in the prop, could not rise and smashed into the hull of the battleship, not leaving so much as a dark blotch on the thick hull.

Lt. Roby fared little better against battleship Nagato. He led his four Dauntlesses straight into the battleship, disregarding the heavy ack-ack fire. Roby had been one of the lucky pilots who carried 500 pound bombs under his wings. Through some miracle, he avoided the ack-ack fire and came over Nagato at 500 feet to unleash his bombs and a stream of

5" rockets. One bomb hit the port side of the ship, blowing away a supply compartment and the other 500 pounder exploded about 25 feet from the bow and tore up a 20 foot section of deck. The rockets hit amidship and erupted three fires that kept Nagato repair crews busy with fire hoses and sand.

These first hits rattled Nagato's gunners, allowing the Dauntlesses from Gambier Bay's Squadron 10 B Flight to unleash their rockets and bombs in relative safety. But, these other Dauntlesses, with mere century bombs, caused only minimal damage as did the strafing fire by B Flight's Hellcats. Fortunately, however, B Flight lost only one of its Dauntlesses and none of its Hellcats.

Lt. Roby ducked into a cloud bank at 7,000 feet with the same disappointing frustration as did the other Avenger pilots of Taffy 3. They simply did not have the heavy bombs and torpedoes to do any real damage against capital ships, and they did not have enough aircraft. The attacks by Huxtable and Roby threw the two battleships out of battle formation, however, as the big ships took evasive action against the attacking planes.

Now came the last American air unit, Composite 68 from Fanshaw Bay with its torpedoes and 500 pound bombs. The Avengers went after the battleships of Batdiv 3, Haruna and Kongo. But, the massive ack-ack fire from the two big battleships not only threw off the aims of the American pilots, but left a wall of obscuring smoke. Lt. Cmdr. Bob Roberts and his Avenger pilots scored only one bomb hit and several rocket hits on the battleships but caused no serious damage. And, disappointingly, not a single one of the four torpedoes scored a hit. Further, the strafing runs by Corsairs did nothing but offer Japanese sailors another chance to shelter themselves from tracer bullets pinging and richocheting off the tough armor plating of their gunpits.

For their efforts, Composite Squadron 68 lost a Dauntless and a Corsair.

The aerial attacks had only lasted a few minutes. Admiral Kurita then looked at his chief of staff with a puzzled look. "I do not see any more aircraft, Tomiji. Is this all the enemy will mount against us? This is not a fraction of the aircraft that struck us yesterday."

Admiral Koyanagi squinted into the broken clouds but he saw nothing more. "Strange, Takeo, strange. We were sure that the enemy fleet included six aircraft carriers. Surely, they could mount more aircraft than this mere pittance they have sent against us."

"There is something else unusual," Admiral Matome Ugaki pointed out. "The enemy aircraft launched few torpedoes against us and most of their bombs were mere light fragmentation bombs. How could this be from fleet carrier aircraft?"

"Perhaps this enemy fleet to the south does not include large, fast carriers," Koyanagi said.

"There is no question of that, Tomiji," Admiral Ugaki shook his head. "They are definitely aircraft carriers."

"Then how do we account for this meagre aerial assault with light armament?" Admiral Koyanagi asked. "Is it possible that we have allowed imagination to subordinate cool judgment? Are there truly American cruisers and battleships to the south? If so, why have they not fired salvos from such capital ships? Surely, their battleships and cruisers can also loosen shellfire from 20,000 to 30,000 meter ranges. Why were we only attacked by destroyers and destroyer escorts?"

"I am perplexed, Tomiji," Kurita said. "Please call 2nd Air Fleet headquarters again. Tell them it is imperative that we get a reconnaisance report on the complement of the enemy fleet that lies to the south of us."

"Yes, Admiral."

Kurita then turned to Admiral Ugaki. "Launch two more float planes, Matome. After the damage we have caused these Yankee air formations, the American airmen may be so grateful to be alive and to return to their carriers that they will have neither the time nor inclination to attack again our float planes."

Admiral Ugaki nodded.

"Meanwhile, we must again reform to renew with all speed our attacks against the enemy fleet."

"Yes, Honorable Kurita," Admiral Tomiji Koyanagi nodded.

Within five minutes, at 0750 hours, an hour after the battle was first joined, and after Taffy 3's tin cans and aircraft had tried to stop the enemy fleet, the 1st Striking Force once more chased after the Taffy 3 baby flat tops.

Chapter Eight

At about 0735 hours, 15 minutes before Admiral Kurita resumed his chase of Taffy 3, Admiral William Sample had launched planes to help out Ziggy Sprague. The southern American Taffy units had wallowed about 40 miles off Surigao Island, some fifty miles east of Surigao Strait, and perhaps 130 miles south of Taffy 3. Before Taffy 3 observers had sighted the Japanese 1st Striking Force, this second group of American CVE's had already sent out dozens of aircraft with torpedoes and 500 pound bombs to attack the cripples of Nishimura's 2nd Striking Force beyond Surigao Strait in the Sulu Sea. These southern Taffys had also sent out numerous planes on CAP, antisubmarine patrol, and ground support missions for the American infantrymen fighting Japanese ground troops in Leyte. In fact, an entire composite squadron had left CVE Marcus Island at 0545 hours to drop 1,000 gallons of water and 1,200 cans of K rations to a 96th Division American infantry company that had found itself isolated from the rest of its battalion.

Thus, when Admiral Sample assured Ziggy Sprague

that he would mount a hundred planes to help out against Kurita's fleet, the southern force deputy commander had clearly exaggerated his capacity to send aid.

Ironically, the work crews of Taffys 1 and 2 from these southern escort carrier forces had been up most of the night to rig torpedoes and fuse heavy bombs. Admiral Thomas Kinkaid, the 7th Fleet commander, had ordered these Avengers to help out Kinkaid's battleship-cruiser force in destroying the cripples from the Japanese 2nd Striking Force now in the Sulu Sea. Unfortunately, by the time Admiral Sample got the call from Admiral Ziggy Sprague, most of the southern Taffy group aircraft, many of them carrying torpedoes and heavy bombs, were out chasing the cripples of the Japanese southern force.

Totally, Admiral William Sample could only mount 31 Avengers and 28 escorting Hellcats to help Ziggy Sprague, with only about a dozen of them carrying torpedoes or 500 pound bombs. Most of the aircraft carried the same 100 pound antipersonnel fragmentation bombs as did the aircraft from Ziggy Sprague's Taffy 3.

And then, even these aircraft that got off did not do so until 0700 hours. Worse, the Avengers and Hellcats from the southern Taffy units had been further delayed because of difficulty in making rendezvous. Thus, the aircraft from Admiral Sample's Taffy units would find difficulty in locating the enemy. They would not make their attacks on Kurita's fleet until about 0800 hours.

Admiral Sample, recognizing the meagre complement of air units he could send out, and realizing their relatively light bomb loads, had given his squadron leaders special instructions:

"You people aren't capable of sinking any of those heavy ships with your light armament. Don't concentrate on one or two ships as they did in the Subayan Sea yesterday. Hit as many ships as you can and simply try to cripple them. That'll force them to break off their attack on Admiral Sprague's carriers and perhaps even prompt them to retire. Halsey can then take care of them when he gets back from the north with his big fleet carriers."

When Sample's 31 Avengers and 28 Hellcats got off, he turned to an aide. "Those few planes will help, but we'll need to send Ziggy Sprague more as soon as we get those other aircraft back from chasing those Japanese cripples."

"They should be back in about an hour," the aide said.

"Good," Sample nodded.

The southern Taffy groups deputy commander could not guess that the Japanese had an astonishing strategem in store for the jeep carriers that lay 130 miles south of the harried Taffy 3.

At the northern tip of Mindanao Island, at 0700 hours, October 25, 1944, Japanese sentinels were looking at the wide Pacific to the east. They were stationed in the town of Surigao that faced Surigao Strait to the north and the Pacific to the east. They scanned the seas and wondered if American surface ships or naval planes would attack Surigao and its nearby airfield, as the Americans had attacked the

Japanese fleets. These sentinels also looked hopefully into the skies for possible Japanese planes that might come north from Davao to hit the Americans, especially U. S. aircraft carriers.

The sentinels grew hopeful when they saw a flight of 12 Japanese planes zooming high over the seaport town on the northeast tip of Mindanao. But, the aircraft formations looked strange. Six of the planes flew in a pair of tight V's while the other six planes hung around the first six in a protective escort pattern. Yet, all 12 planes were Mitsubishi fighter planes. Odd! Why would six fighter planes escort six other fighter planes?

These Japanese sentinels were unaware of an awesome fact: they were looking at two V's of suicide planes, the first during three years of war against the United States in the Pacific.

High above Surigao, at nearly 10,000 feet, Lt. Yosunori Aoki peered from the cockpit of his Zero and studied the clear skies above the broken clouds. He wore perhaps the most somber face of his young life on this 25th day of October in 1944. He looked at his fuel gauge, barely over the ¼ mark, obviously not enough to reach Leyte Gulf and then return to Davao. The gauge reminded Aoki that he was on a one way trip.

Lt. Aoki was a true son of Japan, a loyal servant of the Emperor. His small, wirey frame held perhaps more patriotism for his country than anyone in the Japanese empire. If duty necessitated a deliberate sacrifice of his life in a noble cause, he would do so. For more than 48 hours, he had been preparing

133

himself to die. He had written all the letters: to his parents, to his sisters, to his sweetheart, explaining the need to give up his life. He must die to save Japan, he had written them. They must not grieve for him, not feel remorse for him, not protest his action. His decision to die was necessary and proper. He was, after all, a warrior of Japan, a true Samurai in the Bushido tradition and the Yamato spirit. He had closed his letters with the famous line of the doleful, stirring song of the ancient warriors: " . . . I shall not die peacefully at home."

And yesterday, as word came from Admiral Onishi to prepare the Yamato Special Attack Force, Aoki and his fellow Divine Wind pilots had listened to instructions without fear, apprehension, or regret. Last night, when it appeared they must fly out this morning, they had conducted their ritual: somber pleas to Divine Heaven to welcome them in glory for their sacrifice to the Emperor, supplications to the ancestral spirits to intercede with heaven on their behalf. Then had come the silent, somber toast of water from a canteen, passed among all the pilots of the Yamato Special Attack Force that would fly out today. When the ritual had ended, superiors had offered the Kamikaze pilots anything they wanted before they flew away and died.

But Lt. Aoki, like many others, had asked for nothing: no sumptuous meal or drink, no geisha girls to entertain him, no woman to sleep with, nor any other material comfort. Aoki saw his obligation as a spiritual one and he would confine himself to nourishment of the spirit during the long waiting hours before he snuffed out his life against an enemy aircraft carrier. He had not slept well last night, not because he feared death, but because he feared the mission might be postponed again.

Then, at 0500 hours, when word came from Manila, Lt. Yosonuri Aoki had felt relief. At 0503 hours, he had conducted a final ritual on the Davao airfield before the base commander and before hundreds of Japanese soldiers and airmen who had watched in awe as these first suicide pilots walked to their aircraft for their one way flight to oblivion.

When Lt. Aoki took off, he had circled the field at Davao before he soared over the green jungles, rice fields, winding roads, occasional snaking river, and the small towns like Malaybalay and Butuan. Now, at 0700 hours, Lt. Aoki stared down at the town of Surigao on the northeast coast of Mindanao. Soon, the tip of the huge island disappeared behind him.

The Yamato unit commander looked at the other Zeros on his right and left of the 3 plane V, and he could see the faces of the pilots: cold, sober, staring straight ahead. They had no doubt infused in themselves the same rabid determination as had Yosunori Aoki.

For the next half hour, as the 12 Zeros droned on, the pilots saw no enemy surface ships or enemy aircraft. They were apparently flying towards Leyte Gulf undetected. Finally, a call came to Aoki from the 74 Squadron escort commander.

"We now approach Dinagat Island. The enemy carrier fleet lies some fifty degrees to the east of this island. When we reach Dinagat we will drop in altitude and fly low over the island, and then lower still when we reach the open waters beyond. Our scout planes report six small enemy escort carriers in this area. Your duty is to destroy them, so these enemy carriers cannot interfere with the Honorable Kurita's mission to Leyte Gulf. May I suggest, Lt. Aoki, that you assign an aircraft to each of these enemy vessels."

"Yes, Commander," Lt. Aoki answered.

"When we have passed Dinagat Island, you will hold a 130 degree course which should take you directly into the enemy fleet. We will not resume our 10,000 feet altitude until we come within five or ten minutes of the American carriers. Then, you and your pilots may dive from that height to accomplish your mission." The 74 Squadron commander paused. "I can only add, Lt. Aoki, that I wish you good luck. May the Gods of heaven and the ancestral spirits praise you and the others for your efforts, and may heaven bless you with success." Then: "And now, we will maintain radio silence."

"Yes, Commander," Lt. Aoki said again.

Soon, the six planes of the Yamato Special Attack Force droned over the dense green forests of Dinagat Island. Once beyond Dinagat, Lt. Aoki knew he would be a half hour from target. Still, he felt no perspiration and no tremors inside of him. Lt. Yosunori felt nothing except a will to succeed.

A hundred miles to the east wallowed the Taffy 1 segment of the southern Taffy units. Captain Robert Blick stood on the bridge of jeep carrier USS Santee. He peered out to the open sea, now relatively calm and he studied the other CVE's of Taffy 1 around him: USS Sangamon, Suwannee, Chenango, Saginaw Bay, and Petrof Bay. Then, Captain Blick stared at the mild curls of smoke rising from Taffy 1's screen, destroyers USS Trathen and Hazelwood, along with the smaller DDE's, USS Edmonds, Bull, Rowel, and Eversole.

The six tin cans moved slowly, almost loitering, in a routine shuttle north of the jeep carriers. And why not? There had been no alerts from antisubmarine patrol or CAP's: no Japanese submarines around, no surface ships, and no enemy aircraft. The last of a dozen Avengers and Corsairs had left the deck of Santee only a few minutes ago and had already disappeared to the north to attack the Japanese 1st Striking Force.

Captain Blick relaxed and sipped a cup of coffee and ate a roll that a steward had brought from the galley.

"Do you think we can stop that Jap fleet, Sir?" the steward asked.

"If we get enough planes out," Captain Blick answered.

The Santee commander looked again at the open sea around him and he then sniffed in the cool morning breeze, comfortable in these Pacific waters where dense humidity caused so much distress. Captain Blick looked at his watch: 0747. His aircraft had gone off to the Sulu Sea some time ago to hunt down the Japanese cripples and they should be back soon. As soon as Santee retrieved them, Captain Blick would hastily rearm and refuel them to join other Taffy 1 aircraft in the attack on Kurita's 1st Striking Force.

Aboard the escort carrier USS Suwannee, Captain Warren Johnson, the baby flat top skipper, also stood quietly on the bridge of his vessel. His complement of aircraft included 22 Hellcat fighters and 9 Avenger torpedo bombers. But, Johnson too had launched most of them two hours ago to attack the Japanese surface ship cripples west of Surigao Strait. He could only send out 3 Avengers and a half dozen fighter planes to join the attack on the Japanese surface fleet to the north. Johnson too waited for his planes to return from the Sulu Sea so he could rearm and refuel them for more strikes on the Japanese ships off Samar Island.

At 0750 hours, both Captain Blick aboard Santee and Captain Johnson aboard Suwannee heard the whine of aircraft to the west. Both skippers thought their carrier planes had finally returned. But they saw two of the DDE's on their screen emit heavy puffs of smoke from their stacks and then plow swiftly to the westward before unleashing heavy ack-ack fire from both their 4" and 40MM guns. The aircraft approaching the Taffy 1 carriers were not American planes returning from the Sulu Sea; they were Japanese. Within a few moments the bluejackets of this southern Taffy unit would get a numbing shock.

The Japanese formations, when they came within ten miles of the Taffy jeep carriers, suddenly zoomed upwards and into the thick alto stratus clouds until they leveled off at 10,000 feet. The U. S. sailors expressed surprise because the Japanese usually continued a low level run to make torpedo or low bombing attacks against American ships. Why had these Japanese planes broke and risen high above the clouds to disappear from view? No heavy antiaircraft fire or intercepting planes had bothered them.

Still, the bluejackets took no chances. The sailors of Taffy 1 hurried to battle stations, tightening life jackets around their chests and strapping steel helmets on their heads. Within moments, all gunners had reached 40MM, 20MM, or 5" gun pits to await an enemy aerial attack. Helmsmen prepared for evasive action. For the next several minutes, the sailors heard the drone of Japanese planes above the clouds. They waited alertly, ready to shoot as soon as these interlopers came out of the overcast.

In jeep carrier communication rooms, radio men picked up garble on their sets, apparent TBS talk between Japanese pilots. And in fact, Lt. Aoki was instructing his suicide pilots before they came out of the clouds. Each aircraft would single out an aircraft carrier, while escorting Zeros hung under the clouds to ward off any American CAP interceptor planes. The Yamato Special Attack Force pilots must remember to make their dives vertically and as fast as they could to strike the target with maximum velocity. Such a hard, perpendicular strike would enable the suicide plan to penetrate the carrier deck and lodge in the lower compartments where the bomb explosions would cause more damage.

At 0755, the aircraft of both the Yamato unit and the escorting 74 Squadron came out of the clouds. A barrage of antiaircraft fire greeted them: 5", 4", 3", 40MM, and 20MM guns from the destroyers, destroyer escorts, and the flat tops. The sky under the low clouds thickened with exploding black puffs.

But the heavy flak never deterred the Japanese suicide pilots. After all, every one of the six Kamikaze flyers intended to kill himself and hopefully take a carrier with him.

The first Divine Wind pilot singled out jeep carrier Santee. The loaded Zero, a 250 mg bomb under each wing, arched into position and then dove straight down on Santee. The gunners in the jeep carrier's 40MM gunpit fired frantically at the diving Zero whose pilot released a stream of tracer fire. American sailors scattered, but still looked curiously at the oncoming plane. When would the pilot come out of his dive and drop his bombs before veering away? And could this Zero even come out of such a steep dive?

But, as the Zero came closer, the sailors gaped in horror. The oncoming plane made no attempt to release bombs; nor did the Japanese pilot apparently intend to pull out of his almost vertical dive. Had ack-ack fire killed the pilot so he could not release bombs and veer away? No. Even during the fleeting seconds, none of the gunners on the antiaircraft guns had seen any major damage to the aircraft or evidence of injury to the pilot. Both the pilot and aircraft appeared perfectly sound. God! The Japanese flyer meant to crash his plane deliberately into Santee! The idea horrified the American bluejackets.

True enough! Within a few seconds, the diving Zero smashed nose first onto Santee's forward elevator. The crashing aircraft cut through the deck, blowing a 15 by 30 foot hole before the crumpled Zero came to rest in the hangar deck below. The subsequent explosion from two wing bombs tore holes in the flight deck, started fires below, killed 16 men, and wounded 27 more. Gasoline tanks on the flight deck ignited depth charges that whooshed into flames. Life preservers caught fire as did the clothing and flesh of wounded and slain men.

In the immediate vicinity of Santee's hangar deck lay a menace even worse than this astounding self-destruct pilot. Flames licked toward eight stored 1,000 pound bombs. Fortunately, clean up crews worked fast, despite the possible hazard of new explosions. They doused the flames and quickly jettisoned into the sea the bombs as well as the flaming depth charge cannisters.

The shock from damage and casualties was mild compared to the chilling knowledge that an enemy pilot had intentionally cracked his plane into Santee. The American sailors had rated a macabre first—the first American ship of World War II hit by a Kamikaze.

As flames erupted from Santee, sailors on other carriers shuttled their glances between flaming Santee and the Japanese planes overhead. Then, as a second Zero plunged towards the jeep carrier Suwannee, the flat top commander, Captain Warren Johnson, looked in astonishment as the Zero dove straight for the deck of his ship. Both Johnson and the crew stiffened as Suwannee's ack-ack gunners fired fast and furiously at the plunging aircraft. After witnessing the numbing, deliberate crash on Santee, the sailors aboard Suwannee guessed at once that this second Zero meant to smash into their flat top.

Captain Johnson cried anxiously into his JV. "Hit

that damn thing! Hit it!" Then he turned to his helmsman. "Hard left! Swing our ass! Swing our ass!"

Seemingly, the gunners aboard Suwannee enjoyed better luck than did those aboard Santee. Their heavy fire caught the zooming Zero squarely, knocking off the plane's tail and part of the fusilage. The aircraft spiralled downward, smoking, rolled over in a 45 degree turn, and glided towards CVE Sangamon. With a single shell from her 5" gun, Sangamon's gunners hit the arching, smoking plane some 500 feet from the flight deck, causing the plane to swerve and miss the carrier deck. The aircraft splashed into the sea off the port bow. The Zero's bombs exploded, however, and shrapnel from the blast killed one man in the jeep carrier's forecastle, while more shrapnel punched several holes in the forward area of Sangamon's deck.

Now, a third Zero dove towards Suwannee and the aft gunners again sent heavy 40MM and 20MM fire at the approaching plane, whose pilot also intended to commit suicide in an attempt to destroy the escort carrier. The idea seemed absolutely abhorrent to the American sailors who regarded human life as mankind's most prized possession, even in this life and death struggle of raging war. Suwannee's gunners finally sent a burst of flak that caught the plane under the left wing, knocking off the wing. The Zero arched away and then glided dizzily towards the port quarter of CVE Petrof Bay. However, the plane crashed into the sea, the Zero's bombs failed to explode, and the Zero sank slowly. Jeep carrier Petrof Bay thus avoided any damage or casualties.

142

But, the Zero suicide pilots were not finished. At about 0758 hours, another Kamikaze dove from 8,000 feet. She came towards the stern of Suwannee and once more the harried gunners of the jeep carrier unleashed streams of antiaircraft fire. A hit ignited smoke, but the Zero, despite trailing smoke, continued its plunge. A Hellcat pilot on CAP now jumped the smoking Zero, spewing tracer fire at the Kamakaze. But, the American fighter pilot had intercepted too late. Before the navy pilot could drop the enemy plane out of the sky, the suicide pilot rolled over, dodged the pursuing Hellcat, and came straight towards Suwannee's starboard. The burning Zero reached the flat top and smashed into the deck about 40 feet forward of the aft elevator.

The Zero's engine penetrated the flight deck and the suicide plane's bombs exploded between the top deck and the hanger deck. The blast tore a huge 25 foot hole in the flight deck, injuring a dozen men, killing a dozen more, and tossing another half dozen bluejackets over the side. The explosion also put Suwannee's steering out of commission and knocked out power in the aft elevator. Repair crews swiftly worked on steering and power, while corpsmen quickly tended the wounded. However, the flight deck, with two huge holes, would remain imoperable for the rest of the day, and Suwannee's planes would need to land elsewhere when they returned from both the Sulu Sea and their air strike up north.

One of the two remaining suicide planes dove towards Petrof Bay, whose gunners, with the aid of gunners from DD Trathen, poured heavy fire

143

at the diving plane. One burst hit the Zero squarely, cutting off its wing, and another burst of flak from a 5" gun cut the fuselage in half. The suicide plane burst into flames, its two 250 mg bombs exploded, and metal fragments of the Zero dropped like black confetti before the fragments plopped into the sea.

Now, strangely, two of the escorting Zeros came down from their escort positions and roared towards carrier Sangamon in strafing runs. But, intense antiaircraft fire drove them off, and one of the planes ignited smoke from a flak hit. This damaged plane arched away from the jeep carrier, rose upwards and ducked into the clouds. She was never seen again. Presumably, she wandered somewhere off to the eastward in damaged condition and then fell into the sea, plane and pilot lost forever.

Lt. Yosunori Aoki himself headed for the baby flat top Chenango. As he dove towards the escort carrier, he saw blazing Santee and listing Suwannee. A satisfaction swelled inside of him. His Divine Wind fellow pilots of the Yamato Special Attack Corps had already put two American carriers out of commission. Hopefully, Aoki would disable a third.

Aoki ignored the heavy streams of fire from 20MM and 40MM guns on Chenango's aft. And, in fact, he opened with strafing fire when he came within 2,000 feet of the CVE's deck, scattering American sailors. Soon, DDE Edmonds plied into position to help out Chenango and the DDE sent streams of 3" and 40MM shellfire at Aoki's plane. Within 500 yards of Chenango, several hits scored on the Zero, emitting flames that streamed from the engine cowling. The hits also spun the Zero out of its dive.

Aoki tried to climb to resume his straight dive on Chenango's flight deck. But, within a few hundred yards of the CVE, a hit shattered the cockpit, shrapnel struck Aoki's chest and arms, pain shot through his body, and he quickly fell into semi-consciousness. The Zero rapidly lost altitude but leveled out, glided downward, and skidded along the surface of the water to within a hundred yards of DDE Edmonds.

Sailors aboard Edmonds swiftly lowered a boat and hurried to the slowly sinking Zero. The bluejackets were not particularly humane, but curiosity had overwhelmed them. They had to see a Japanese pilot who would deliberately kill himself to put a jeep carrier out of business.

So, ironically, Lt. Yosunori Aoki survived. The American sailors pulled the unconscious suicide pilot from his sinking plane and brought him back to Edmonds, a most humiliating fate for a Samurai warrior—prisoner of war. U. S. authorities would watch Aoki continually during his months of captivity lest he attempt hari-kari suicide. But, a year later, by the time of his release from military custody, Aoki had lost his fervor for suicide. He would become a valuable source of information for future historians who studied the details and philosophy of the Kamikaze pilot.

By 0800 hours, the first Kamikaze assault of World War II was over. Five Yamato Special Attack Force pilots had died and one had been captured. Two jeep carriers were out of commission. The escorting Zero pilots quickly sent back exaggerated reports to Davao (just as the Americans often exaggerated). The Japanese 74 Escort Squadron flyers claimed that six suicide pilots had sunk four of the jeep carriers of Taffy 1.

Nonetheless, with two heavily damaged baby flat tops, Taffy 1 could not send more planes north to help out Admiral Ziggy Sprague. Admiral Sample would be too busy detouring returning aircraft from Santee and Suwannee to the four remaining jeep carriers of Taffy 1. Further, these southern Taffy escort carriers needed to hastily store their own returning aircraft to make room for the planes from the two damaged jeep carriers.

Over a hundred miles to the north, by 0755 hours, 1st Striking Force had shortened range again on Ziggy Sprague's Taffy 3 escort carriers, with Desron 10 once more preparing to launch torpedoes.

Then, out of the south came the Avengers and Hellcats of Taffy 1. Once more, commanders on Kurita's ships found themselves diverted from their primary mission. Again ack-ack gunners spewed ack-ack fire and again helmsmen veered and twisted in evasive action.

The few American planes carrying torpedoes failed to score a single hit and the other American aircraft of Taffy 1 had bombed inaccurately due to intense and accurate ack-ack fire, and due to adept maneuvering by Japanese helmsman. So again, except for a heavy hit on cruiser Chikuma and minor hits on the other ships, this new aerial attack did little damage to the 1st Striking Force. For their trouble, the aircraft of the southern Taffy units lost four Avengers and three Hellcats.

As soon as the air attack ended, Kurita acted swiftly. By 0805 Kurita had once again reformed

146

his ships at or near his Number 19 battle disposition to continue his pursuit and attack of the Taffy 3 jeep carriers. In fact, the cruisers of Crudiv 7 and the battleships of Batdiv 1 had already resumed fire with 8", 14", and 18" guns.

Chapter Nine

At the same 0805 hours, Admiral Ziggy Sprague stared once more from the bridge of Fanshaw Bay and watched the new approach of the Japanese fleet. His own carrier and the other baby flat tops of Taffy 3 had been darting about the sea like small fish trying to escape predators. He looked stiffly at Dave Johnson who stood erect in the same wheelhouse of Fanshaw Bay and also waited for the inevitable.

Sprague then turned to his chief of staff, Captain Jim Carsen. "Any word yet? Anything at all on the prospects of help?"

"I'm sorry, Sir," the Taffy 3 chief of staff answered. "7th Fleet battleships and cruisers are just entering Surigao Strait and the 3rd Fleet carriers are still hours away from even aircraft launch."

Sprague licked his lips and then wiped perspiration from his forehead. "What about the Taffys of the southern units?"

"They've just made a strike and they expect to make another one in about two hours."

"Two hours?" Ziggy Sprague huffed.

"That's what Admiral Sample's aide says," Carsen answered.

Sprague scowled and he then pointed to Captain David Johnson. "They don't understand. None of those bastards understand: not Kinkaid, not Halsey, and none of those people in the southern Taffy groups. Bill Sample is dragging his ass. He should have had more bombers up here long before this."

Captain David Johnson did not answer. But, neither the Fanshaw Bay skipper nor the Taffy 3 commander knew that Admiral Sample had just been subjected to the numbing shock of a Kamikaze attack that now put Taffy 1 in serious trouble.

Sprague took a deep breath and then sighed. "What about our own planes? Have they done anything worthwhile?"

"I don't know, Admiral," Captain Carsen answered.

Sprague peered again to the north through binoculars and once more he saw the Japanese ships moving back in column, even as the enemy capital ships picked up speed to close again on the Taffy 3 jeep carriers. A sense of defeat sobered Sprague's round face. The tin can attacks had done little to stop the advance of the Japanese fleet and, apparently, the air attacks from both his own Taffy 3 squadrons and those planes from the southern Taffy units had failed to slow down materially the enemy fleet. The Japanese would soon again be in proper battle order to assail Taffy 3. Kalinin Bay had already suffered serious hits, with her flight deck punched with holes and her speed reduced. Sprague guessed that his other five jeep carriers would soon sustain the same kind of damage or even worse—destruction.

Sprague took a deep, choppy breath and again turned to his aide. "Get Captain Thomas on the TBS. See if he can lay more smoke."

"Yes Sir," Captain James Carsen answered.

Now, Ziggy Sprague scanned the skies once more, looking for his aircraft. The planes had obviously finished their attacks by now, but they were nowhere in sight and the enemy flotilla was again on the move. Panic struck Sprague for a fleeting moment. Could the enemy fleet have shot down all the Taffy 3 planes? No! Nothing that disastrous. The aircraft simply hadn't returned yet.

Then, Sprague suddenly remembered that Kalinin Bay was in no condition to retrieve planes. Captain Williamson's aircraft would need to land somewhere else. He turned to Captain Carsen. "Call the other carriers and tell them to expect a few extra planes because Kalinin Bay will have no way of taking on its own returning aircraft."

"Aye, Sir."

"When you find out which carriers can take Kalinin Bay's aircraft, raise the flight leader of Squadron 3 and tell him to send his returning planes to such carriers."

"Aye, Sir," the chief of staff said again.

However, before the aide picked up the TBS, an 8" shell from cruiser Suzuya struck and shuddered Fanshaw Bay, blowing apart the flag office, killing the signalman and wounding his two assistants. The hit almost knocked Admiral Sprague, Captain Johnson, and Captain Carsen off their feet, along with others in the wheelhouse. But they managed to grab onto something and hold on.

"Goddamn it," Sprague yelled. He looked at the helmsman. "Evasive maneuver! Evasive maneuver!"

"I'm doing the best I can, Sir."

"Well try harder," Sprague barked.

"Aye, Sir."

But, a moment later, another 8" shell squarely struck the forward area of the flight deck, ripped away a full 200 foot section of deck, and damaged over a dozen of the structural beams supporting the flight deck. Repair crews hurried out to pull back launch lines before the lines caught fire. The second hit had also prompted those on the bridge to take cover. When they finally straightened, Captain David Johnson peered from the bridge window at the damage. Then he picked up his JV.

"#3 repair crew, #3 repair crew: get that deck patched. On the double! We've got aircraft coming back and they may return any minute."

"But Sir," somebody from the #3 repair crew answered, "the supports are severed. I don't know how we can repair them."

Then, suddenly, another 8" Japanese shell struck Fanshaw Bay and wrecked the catapult track beyond the bridge, warping the walk from the bridge to midship, and demolishing the drive gear of the anchor windlass. Captain Johnson rushed to starboard, peered at the maze of twisted metal and once again picked a JV phone.

"Forecastle repair crew! #6 repair crew!"

"Aye aye."

"The cat track from the bridge is wrecked. Get

151

rope ladders down. If we have to abandon the wheel-house, we'll need a parachute to reach the main deck."

"Right away, Captain," somebody answered.

Captain Johnson leaned from the bridge and craned his neck to watch the men above him scramble like busy ants to get the rope ladders down. The Fanshaw Bay skipper then peered out to sea and watched the spray of colored geysers exploding around his jeep carrier, some of them quite close. Johnson had relaxed for only a moment, however, before the next 8 incher slammed into the hull some eight feet below the water line. The hit opened a one foot hole and shuddered the baby flat top so violently that every man in the wheelhouse fell off his feet.

Within seconds, however, Captain Johnson was erect again and once more screaming into his JV. "Damage control! Damage control!"

"We've got a breach in the hull on the port side," Lt. Hank Cayot, the chief repair officer, answered the captain. "The A1-W compartment is flooding and we've got a crew trying to seal the breach."

"Make it fast," Johnson said.

"We'll do our best, Sir," Cayot answered.

"You've got to make certain," Johnson said. "If we get a list or too much water, we'll lose speed and maneuverability. We'll be dead."

"Aye, Sir," Lt. Cayot answered.

Captain David Johnson now looked at Admiral Clifton Sprague who only stared somberly at the horizon to the northwest. The Japanese had clearly closed range. The admiral dropped his binoculars, letting the glasses dangle from his neck. "Goddamn it," he cursed under his breath.

"We'll make it, Ziggy, we'll make it," Captain Johnson said.

Ziggy Sprague did not answer.

Then, a new salvo of 8 inch shells, probably from Chikuma, sailed towards Fanshaw Bay. Four missed but one shell struck squarely amidship. The explosion tore another hole in the flight deck, started another fire, and buckled the platform deck. The hit had also weakened the aviation gas tanks under the platform deck. As Captain Johnson ran to the port side of the bridge for a look, he got a call from Lt. Cayot.

"Captain, Sir, we'll need to jettison fire bombs. Those ruptured gas tanks are starting to leak, and we've had some fires. We'll blow apart if gasoline flames reach the magazine. Please, Sir, permission to jettison fire bombs."

"You're the man down there, Lieutenant," Captain Johnson answered. "If that's what you think we need to do, then do it."

"Aye, Sir," Cayot answered.

Then Johnson called the engine room. "Can you give us any more speed?"

"We're at 17 knots, Sir, and the way the helmsman is weaving and twisting this ship, we might rupture seams in the weakened section of the hull. Sir, I suggest speed reduction to 15 knots with these evasive tactics."

"No," Johnson answered sharply.

Then, a big 14" shell struck behind the forecastle, blowing away the resistor room, the after state room, and the overhead state room, while killing and wounding over a dozen bluejackets. Those in the wheelhouse cowered instinctively as debris fell from above, dropped past the wheelhouse, and scattered on the flight deck, chopping out a few more holes.

Johnson once more picked up his JV. "Clear the deck of rubble! Clear deck of rubble; dump it overboard!"

"Yes Sir," a repair crew chief answered.

And suddenly, another hit somewhere astern shook the ship, ruptured the hull's #18 frame, and smashed the #26 bulkhead. Johnson peered anxiously about his flat top, wondering where the latest hit had struck. Then, he got a call.

"Captain, this is the fire room. The hull and two bulkheads are gone, and we've got small fires. If flames reach those gas tanks, the whole stern could go up and maybe blow away."

"Get out the fires as first priority," Johnson cried into the JV. "Then brace the ruptures as best you can."

"Aye Aye, Sir."

Now, Captain Johnson licked his lips and then looked about the bridge. Everyone here responded to the Fanshaw Bay skipper with silent, sober faces. Johnson then grinned to break the tension.

"We'll make it, we'll make it." When nobody answered Johnson, the captain turned to Admiral Sprague. "We'll get help soon, Ziggy, and we'll make it."

"Sure," Sprague scowled, "if we come up with a miracle somewhere." He looked at Captain Car-

154

sen. "Call Admiral Sample again. Tell him he's got to send us more planes. He's got to."

"Aye Sir," the Taffy 3 aide said.

Fanshaw Bay and Kalinin Bay had not been the only baby flat tops taking punishment. Aboard Gambier Bay, Captain Bill Viewig stared apprehensively from the wheelhouse at the reforming enemy ships and the resumption of Japanese shellfire. Gambier Bay, at the head of the Taffy 3 retreat oval, had been scudding into the wind where the smoke from the tin can screen drifted to starboard and aft, thus affording little protection. So, the jeep carrier had been quite exposed.

From the onset of Japanese shellfire, Gambier Bay had been a principal target. Miraculously, no salvos had yet struck the flat top thanks to Cmdr. George Gellhorn, Gambier Bay's navigator. Until 0800 hours, he had done an excellent job of evasive action. Gellhorn had alternately maneuvered CVE Gambier Bay from one side of base course to the other to avoid Japanese shells. When a salvo crept towards Gambier Bay, Gellhorn had slowed drastically to fall into the position of the recently missed salvo, correctly assuming the Japanese had calculated the speed and course of the flat top. The enemy would then likely send its next salvo to a plotted arc based on such calculated speed and course.

Gellhorn would then find the next salvo exploding in front of the baby flat top. Then the navigator maneuvered the ship to starboard or port and watched the adjusted Japanese shellfire explode geysers off the port or starboard side. The navigator's ability to anticipate the next flight of a Japanese Crudiv 7 salvo had enabled him to keep exposed Gambier Bay healthy for more than an hour. Further, Gambier Bay had enjoyed two respites from Japanese gunners, first when the Desron 46 tin cans disrupted the Japanese Crudiv 7 and Desron 10 columns, and again when the Taffy aircraft had made their attacks on the 1st Striking Force.

By 0810 hours, with the Japanese closing again, the enemy vessels of Crudiv 7 had once more zeroed in on Gambier Bay. Colored shells exploded in Gambier Bay's wake, following the zig zagging CVE. And, by 0813 hours, the Japanese had apparently figured out Gellhorn's maneuvers. The jeep carrier caught its first real hit, a strike on the flight deck that punched a huge hole in the forward section of the ship.

"Get the flight deck repaired, get it repaired," Captain Viewig cried from the bridge. Then, he turned to Cmdr. George Gellhorn. "Hard left, hard left."

"Aye Sir," Gellhorn answered, before he ordered the helmsman to spin the wheel.

However, the enemy now had the current range and bearing of Gambier Bay, and the next salvo of shells, from cruiser Chikuma, straddled the CVE's flight deck, with three of the shells hitting squarely on topside. The blasts ripped out a full 30 yard length of deck and started fires. Repair crews rushed forward with hoses and sand but the fires grew rapidly out of control.

"Repair crew! Repair crew!" Captain Viewig cried into the JV. "Get the deck, forward! On the double!" He then turned to Gellhorn. "Okay, Commander, hard left. Take a hard left."

156

"Aye, Sir," the navigator answered.

For the next few minutes, Gellhorn and his helmsman successfully evaded new salvos. But then, at 0817 hours, an eight inch shell from cruiser Tone struck the jeep carrier at the waterline of Gambier Bay's port side, and exploded with such force that the blast tore away the plating of the forward engine room and opened a four feet gap some twelve feet below the water line. Sea water poured into the engine room like an unrestrained flood, and within a minute water had reached the firebox of the boiler and snuffed out all power. Repair crews could barely seal the compartment to stop flooding, much less make engine repairs. The ship quickly listed 20 degrees to port.

And, of course, the knocked out engine room abruptly dropped Gambier Bay's speed from 17 to 11 knots. The jeep carrier quickly fell behind the rest of the Taffy 3 oval. Further, the heavy water intake had drastically lessened Lt. Gellhorn's ability to maneuver the ship. Gambier Bay had become an almost stationary target in the middle of the Philippine Sea.

Aboard Suzuya, Admiral Kazutaka Shiraishi looked gleefully at the burning, listing Gambier Bay. "We will concentrate on this crippled carrier and complete her destruction. Order all vessels of Crudiv 7 to train fire on this American vessel."

"Yes, Honorable Shiraishi," his aide answered.

Soon, not only Suzuya and Tone, but also Chikuma and crippled Kumano aimed their turret guns on the disabled jeep carrier. The cruisers closed to almost 2,000 yards and now pummelled Gambier

Bay at nearly point blank range.

An 8" shell knocked out the second engine room of Gambier Bay, leaving the U. S. jeep carrier dead in the water. Then came a series of hits on the flight deck, punching more holes on the flat top and erupting more fires. Repair crews frantically put out fires, but the flames erupted again and again, making the job impossible.

Within a minute, three more salvos whooshed into Gambier Bay. One 8 incher hit the island structure and knocked out steering. Hit #12 split the vessel's skin on the same listing port side to accelerate flooding and list. The next 8 incher started fires in the forward elevator and in the hangar deck. And now, repair crews ignored the uncontrolled flames and frantically sprinkled water on the magazines lest they catch fire and explode.

Captain Viewig rightly suspected that his ship was beyond salvation. Still, he barked orders into the wheelhouse JV. "Get out fires! Jettison anything that might explode. Seal flooding. Seal flooding!"

Meanwhile, Destroyers Heermann and Johnson both came to Gambier Bay's side. Heermann closed to the starboard of the CVE, now burning amidship and listing to 30 degrees. Heermann opened with forward 5" guns, firing salvos at cruiser Chikuma. The heavy cruiser quickly turned in a tight circle and shifted fire on Heermann. Meanwhile, Cmdr. Ernie Cherokee Evans, minus two fingers, opened with 5" guns on the Japanese cruiser column. The spunky Johnson closed to less than 2,000 yards and sent several 5" hits towards Tone.

The cruiser commander, however, ignored Johnson completely and continued fire on Gambier Bay.

The Tone commander would later regret his decision to snub little Johnson.

Meanwhile, the salvos from Heermann, Johnson, and the single 5" fire from Gambier Bay had drawn cruisers Haguro and Chokai of Crudiv 5 towards the trio of lagging American ships. Desron 2 had also swept forward after the trio of vessels from Taffy 3. Soon, these other ships were also firing at the two American destroyers and the crippled Gambier Bay. An array of colored geysers—red, yellow, green, blue, purple—splashed about the two DD's and the CVE.

While Heermann and Johnson could take good evasive action against the fast and heavy Japanese fire, crippled Gambier Bay had become too immobilized to last. Soon, an 8" shell from short range knocked out the last of Gambier Bay's power. Japanese shells also knocked out radar and opened more holes in the CVE's hull. The listing jeep carrier burned furiously. 133 men aboard Gambier Bay were already dead or wounded. Captain Bill Viewig and Cmdr. George Gellhorn knew that Gambier Bay was finished. Sadly, somberly, Captain Viewig picked up his JV.

"All stations, now hear this; this is the captain. Destroy all documents. Destroy all documents at once."

Men throughout the ship understood the order and they waited for the next order—abandon ship.

Aboard flag cruiser Suzuya, Admiral Shiraishi

was satisfied that Gambier Bay was dead. He then ordered his cruisers to now concentrate on the other jeep carriers and to ignore the two American destroyers, Heermann and Johnson.

Leading the way towards the remaining five carriers, among whom Kalinin Bay and Fanshaw Bay were quite battered, was heavy cruiser Chokai of Desron 2. Sailors aboard jeep carrier White Plains sighted Chokai on a 240 degree bearing, just off Asgad Point, Samar, at a distance of some 15 miles.

"Enemy ship off port aft," the lookout of CVE White Plains reported.

Captain Dave Sullivan, the White Plains skipper, peered through binoculars and he brazenly ordered fire from the baby flat top's 5" gun on the fantail. The American gunners sent several 5 inchers at Chokai and one shell decommissioned a forward turret while another shell put an engine temporarily out of commission.

The commander of Chokai, Captain Keho Ariga, was incensed by the hits from White Plains. "Idiots!" he barked into his radio phone to the gunnery officer. "How could you allow such damage from a Yankee carrier?"

"We will respond at once, Captain," the gunnery officer said.

Then, even on its one properly operating engine, Chokai plowed forward at 20 knots and soon closed to 9,000 yards, while other Japanese cruisers also closed on White Plains. When a new five inch shell from White Plains hit Chokai again and knocked out an antenna, the Japanese cruiser increased speed in its chase of the baby flat top. Chief gunnery mate Bill Jenkins in the White Plains aft gun pit cried to his gun crew:

"Hold on a little longer, boys. We're suckin' them into 40MM range."

Within the next few minutes, as staccatos of 8" shells boomed from the Japanese cruiser guns, the men aboard cowered. The bluejackets counted nearly 200 colored geysers splashing around their jeep carrier, including some 14" geysers from battleships that rose a hundred feet into the air. But, not a single Japanese shell struck the jeep carrier. White Plains obviously possessed some miraculous lucky charm; or, carrier hits on Chokai had so rattled the Japanese gunners that they shot erratically. Perhaps, when Japanese tempers cooled, luck would run out for White Plains.

Meanwhile, bluejackets aboard CVE Kitkun Bay had gaped in awe as Kalinin Bay, Fanshaw Bay, and Gambier Bay took punishing hits from Japanese naval guns, with Gambier Bay obviously going down. The men of Kitkun Bay rightfully guessed they could not forever escape the same kind of punishment.

The first 8" salvo that truly rattled the crew of Kitkun Bay came at 0815 but did not cause serious damage. However, exploding shrapnel spewed over the stern and ignited a pair of oxygen tanks that repair crews quickly brought under control. Another explosion, 50 yards aft of the jeep carrier, injured several sailors from flying shrapnel, but not fatally. In return, the gunners on Kitkun Bay's fantail sent several 5" shells at the Desron 10 destroyers now closing fast. One 5 incher hit destroyer Urakaze, starting a fire on its #1 turret and bringing a cheer from the jeep carrier bluejackets.

But the Japanese gunners on Urakaze considered the hit an affront. The destroyer's gunners sent two 5" salvos at Kitkun Bay with deadly accuracy, ripping up the flight deck of the American CVE and leaving the deck potholed. Fortunately, the hits were mere 5 inchers and did not start major fires. Still, the crew of Kitkun Bay wondered if they could repair the deck to retrieve planes.

St. Lo, the last of the six jeep carriers in Taffy 3, had enjoyed the same good luck as White Plains, but she had been on the southward in the initial south by southeast run by Taffy 3, and she was now on the westward of the new south, by southwest run — quite obscured by the Japanese warships. Tall columns of colored spouts continually erupted astern and left of St. Lo, but during the first hours not a single shell struck the jeep carrier. The sailors aboard had merely gaped at the geysers, ranging in 100 feet heights from the battleship shells to mere 10 feet heights from 5" shells.

CVE St. Lo had originally been commissioned CVE Midway. However, when the U. S. Navy decided to give a big new fast fleet carrier the name Midway, the navy changed the name of the jeep carrier to St. Lo. The sailors on the ship did not like this name change, as old bluejackets often said such name changes brought bad luck. Up to now, the name change had brought good luck to CVE St. Lo.

Still, the Japanese had not completely missed St. Lo. One near miss 8 incher splashed such heavy water on the catwalk of the aft deck that three sailors were almost thrown overboard. Another near miss scattered shrapnel over the flight deck and wounded several bluejackets. And soon, destroyers from Desron 10 straddled St. Lo with several 5" salvos that caused damage to a locker room and to a storage compartment.

At 0820 hours, Admiral Susuma Kimura, from the flag of Desron 10, light cruiser Yahagi, peered through his binoculars at the scampering jeep carriers. "They have been fortunate so far," he said to Yahagi's commander. "It appears we have thus far only damaged seriously three of the carriers."

"There is still time," Captain Masi Yoshimura answered. "We are still closing range to launch massive torpedo attacks. Such an attack will complete the destruction of this American carrier fleet."

"Let us hope so," Admiral Kimura answered.

The Desron 10 commander then peered through his binoculars to study burning and listing Gambier Bay. He then turned to Captain Yoshimura. "Maintain speed and course. When we have closed to 10,000 meters, we will launch our torpedoes."

"Yes, Admiral," Captain Yoshimura answered.

On battleship Yamato, both Admirals Kurita and Ugaki also peered through their binoculars at the burning Kalinin Bay, the damaged Fanshaw Bay, and the flaming, listing Gambier Bay.

"Are we closing range?" Kurita asked.

"Yes, Admiral," chief of staff Tomiji Koyanagi answered. "Our Crudiv 7 and Desron 10 divisions are almost within 10,000 meters of the enemy carriers. Admiral Kimura will soon launch torpedoes. Meanwhile, all vessels continue to fire on the enemy vessels."

Kurita nodded and then scanned the sky. "I see no more American aircraft. And I am puzzled because I have seen no aircraft from our own 2nd Air Fleet."

"We still cannot raise the 2nd Air Fleet headquarters in Manila," Toyanagi said.

For two or three minutes, Kurita and Ugaki continued to stare at the retreating carriers and the dead in the water, sinking Gambier Bay. Meanwhile, the roar of 18" guns even shuddered the mighty Yamato as shells boomed towards the American baby flat tops. Then a radio man brought a message to the bridge and handed the slip of paper to Admiral Tomiji Koyanagi.

"A message from Admiral Fukudome, Admiral."

Koyanagi took the message and read. Then he frowned.

"Is Admiral Fukudome finally sending aircraft?" Admiral Kurita asked.

"I think so, Admiral," Koyanagi answered, "but this message is both puzzling and surprising and, I suppose, quite pleasant."

"I do not understand," Kurita said.

"Admiral Fukudome reports that another American carrier fleet lay some 100 miles south of this one that we have taken under fire. The Honorable Fukudome said he has attacked this second carrier fleet with a special attack air unit and the aircraft destroyed the enemy carriers."

164

"I am not familiar with this new special attack air force that Admiral Fukudome speaks of," the 1st Striking Force commander said.

"Admiral Fukudome says that another special attack air unit will arrive in about two hours to support us," Admiral Koyanagi continued. "He is sure this second attack force will destroy the American carrier fleet we have taken under attack, just as the first special force destroyed the enemy carrier fleet to the south."

"What is this special attack force that Admiral Fukudome speaks of?" Admiral Ugaki asked, frowning. "How can such a force destroy an enemy carrier fleet, when a hundred aircraft yesterday could not even damage such an enemy fleet?"

"I do not know," Koyanagi shook his head.

"We must simply get an explanation of this so-called special attack force," Kurita said.

"I will try to raise once again Admiral Fukudome," Koyanagi said.

"Let us hope we succeed this time," Kurita said.

Chapter Ten

By 0820, 15 minutes after the 1st Striking Force had resumed its assault on Taffy 3, Gambier Bay was belching her last whirls of fire and smoke, and no man aboard the CVE any longer doubted that she would sink below the blue waters of the Philippine Sea. As Gambier Bay listed, foundered, and burned, the men aboard the CVE's of Taffy 3 craned their necks, but they could not see the survivors of Gambier Bay scrambling over the sides. The jeep carrier had fallen too far behind and the ship had become almost totally enveloped in smoke.

The other carriers of Taffy 3 continued their snake dance in the waters northeast of Leyte Gulf, maneuvering frantically to avoid further punishment from the booming 18", 14" and 8" shells from Kurita's battleships and cruisers. Captain Bill Viewig, commander of Gambier Bay, could expect no help from anyone else in Taffy 3 for the other CVE's were now far to the south while they desperately tried to avoid the fate of Gambier Bay.

By 0822 hours, Captain Viewig stood stiffly on the bridge of the fatally hit escort carrier. He shouted orders into a JV as he squinted through the dense smoke and recoiled from the hot fires roaring over the CVE's open deck. He finally turned to those on the bridge with him.

"All right, you've done all you could; get off the ship with the others."

"But Captain," Cmdr. George Gellhorn said, "what about yourself?"

"Never mind me," Viewig answered his navigator. "Get down there and help the others to abandon ship."

Then, Gellhorn, the helmsman, and the bridge officer scrambled down the life lines from the open gangwalk of the bridge to reach the decks below, now palled in dense smoke. By the time they were out of sight, Captain Viewig himself knew he could do nothing more on the bridge and he prepared to abandon ship himself. However, the dense, noxious smoke had already climbed up the lifeline to the bridge area. Then, another shattering explosion from a new 8" shell knocked away another chuck of bridge structure and threw the Gambier Bay skipper off his feet.

Captain Bill Viewig then left the bridge and weaved along the crumpled catwalk, coughing from the dense smoke while he groped his way towards the flight deck ladder. But suddenly, he walked into nothing and fell a dozen feet to a lower catwalk because dense smoke had obscured the view of the missing piece of walk that had been blown away by a Japanese shell. Now, Viewig nearly choked from the hot, gaseous smoke and he winced from a pain in his leg and hip. Still, he struggled to his feet and limped away. Then, he fell again—much further this time, and he was certain he was dropping to his death. Instead, fifty feet later, he plopped hard into the sea. His helmet almost choked the captain as he hit the water, but he came up quickly and felt revived by the plunge into the sea.

Captain Bill Viewig looked about him, and saw a strange, well organized scene. Survivors of Gambier Bay had lashed together seven or eight floater nets, life rafts, and sections of deck planking—making one long rescue train of floating paraphernalia. Cmdr. George Gellhorn and a gunnery officer, Lt. William Buderus, were directing men from the side of the ship to the improvised, elongated raft. Soon enough, Cmdr. Gellhorn yelled to Captain Viewig, who also came aboard one of the rafts.

Captain Bill Viewig sighed in relief, but then a horrible thought struck him: Cmdr. Ed Huxtable was out somewhere with 19 planes. If he escaped Japanese antiaircraft fire, where would Huxtable and his pilots go? Where would they land? Viewig squinted into the sky, but he saw no signs of aircraft under the low clouds. If the aircraft were up there, above the clouds, the captain could not hear them above the din of shouting men, the concussion of Japanese shells, and the belching, crackling fire, or dense hissing smoke about his doomed carrier.

Those aboard other jeep carriers were in no immediate danger of sinking, but the crews were hardly optimistic. Captain Tom Williamson of Kalinin Bay had the dual problem of keeping his ship afloat and avoiding the continued array of shells from Japanese warships. Williamson's CVE, the first of the Taffy

3's ships to suffer damage, was listing to port from the hit that had opened a hole on the port waterline. And, among the fires aboard, the flames from the burning aviation lubrication room emitted a sickening, oily odor. Repair crews, despite the list and fire, were trying to repair the holes in the deck and clear the debris from the machine shop. Other Kalinin Bay sailors worked to repair the ruptured forward elevator and the wrecked I-beams that supported the elevator.

From the bridge, where he blinked from thick smoke, Williamson cried to repair crews through a JV amplifier. "Get out those fires on the aft! Get that debris cleared from port side. Get those oil cans over the side before they catch fire. Throw all bombs overboard before they explode and blow us all to hell."

Occasionally, Williamson lowered his head and cowered, when another whistling shell struck Kalinin Bay to shudder the CVE again, or when a near miss sent up a new spray of briney sea.

And, like Viewig, Captain Tom Williamson also wondered about his aircraft from Composite Squadron 3. Cmdr. Bill Keighley had gone off with 18 planes. Where would the Avengers and Hellcats land if they survived the furious fire from Japanese antiaircraft? The flight deck was a mess. The Kalinin Bay skipper scanned the sky, looking for his planes, but he saw nothing.

Williamson had already had 20 men killed and 50 wounded from the array of solid hits on Kalinin Bay. But upstairs — aircraft running out of gas and nowhere to go. The thought sent a tremor through Williamson's tall, muscular frame. He squinted again at the smoldering segment of deck and the group of repair crews who rushed about the battered surface like stampeding ants as they carried fire hoses, sand pails, or sundry tools. But, Tom Williamson feared the worst. He was sure his ship would go down, just as the Gambier Bay was going down.

The Kalinin Bay skipper cried into his JV again. "Get those fires on the forward. On the forward! Get them out!"

"Yes, Sir," a cry came from a salty chief.

"Captain, some coffee?" somebody suddenly said.

Captain Williamson turned, nodded to the steward and took the hot coffee. After a heavy gulp, he suddenly grinned. "Where the hell did you get coffee with all this confusion going on?"

The steward smiled. "Just enjoy it, Sir."

"Yeah—while we can," Williamson suddenly sobered. Then, he shouted orders through the JV phone amplifier, once more urging repair crews to keep Kalinin Bay afloat.

Some 1,000 yards off the Kalinin Bay's starboard, the CVE Kitkun Bay weaved and heaved on its ocean dance to avoid the screaming shells that continued to pelt the Taffy 3 jeep carriers. Her skipper, Captain Johnny Whitney, had considered himself lucky. Of the dozens of shells that came his way, only a half dozen had struck Kitkun Bay. Unfortunately, the hits had torn up his flight deck, leaving the vessel useless as a landing area for the 16 Avengers and 12 Hellcats under the command of Cmdr. Bob Fowler, leading the CVE's Composite Squadron 5. Whitney thus concentrated on deck repair so he could retrieve his aircraft. He personally left the bridge and moved about the flight deck.

"Bring more plates; more plates," he barked to a repair crew.

"Sir, we're trying to find some," an MM/2 answered. "There just aren't any more around."

"Then cut some from a bulkhead or gunwale or some other non-vital area of the ship. We've got to repair this to bring in returning planes."

The MM/2 restrained a scowl. The Kitkun Bay commander was mad. Did the Captain really believe he could repair the flight deck and save this ship? Better the captain should order abandon ship, while most of the crew were still alive. The MM/2 glanced at the open sea where only smoke, fire, and erupting geysers from Japanese shell explosions lay in every direction. The machinist mate expected death blows from the Japanese heavy warships at any moment. The enemy ships were closing and when those cruisers and battleships got near enough, the big 8" and 18" shells would tear Kitkun Bay to pieces, as the enemy naval guns had already finished off Gambier Bay and threatened to send Kalinin Bay to the bottom also. Still, the MM/2 did not argue with the captain. He hurried off on what he considered a senseless mission.

Captain Whitney, meanwhile, ran to another segment of the deck to question another repair crew. "How's it coming, Chief?"

"We've got this section of deck repaired, Sir," the chief answered, "but to tell the truth, I don't know how much good it'll do. We're still catching hits and a lot 'a near misses. They're gonna get us sooner or later, Sir."

171

"Just keep working and hope for the best."

"Yes, Sir."

But, like the machinist mate, this grizzly repair crew chief also scowled after the departing Captain Johnny Whitney. The chief also squinted at the pall of smoke and exploding geysers around Kitkun Bay. He thought he could even see the flash of gunfire from the Japanese cruisers. The chief, too, expected nothing short of total disaster for this small Taffy 3 jeep carrier force, and for the countless ships in Leyte Gulf, as well as for the thousands of GI's on the Leyte beaches. The chief almost hoped a Japanese shell snuffed out his life so he would not witness the final, horrible fate in Leyte Gulf.

The chief directed his crew for another ten minutes, cowering and ducking with each near miss that sent up new geysers of water or sprayed shrapnel around Kitkun Bay. Then, suddenly, the MM/2 and four other sailors thumped a huge 4x8 steel plate near the chief.

"Here's the plate," the MM/2 said.

The grizzly chief frowned. "What the hell is that thing for?"

The machinist mate shrugged. "The captain says we're going to repair a hole in the flight deck on the starboard quarter."

"Shit," the chief cursed, "he's crazy; he's goddamn crazy. You'd be better off finding yourselves a life raft. It won't be long before you'll need it — if you're still alive, that is."

The machinist mate did not answer the chief.

The same mixture of apprehension and resignation prevailed on the other jeep carriers, for the crews on these companion CVE's of Taffy 3 also recognized their precarious, perhaps hopeless plight.

The CVE St. Lo had yet to suffer a direct hit, experiencing only shrapnel sprays from straddles and near misses, mostly from the Japanese destroyers that hounded her. Despite her good health, however, St. Lo still danced her evasive jig over the sea. St. Lo's aircraft, 22 planes, had left the carrier at 0600 on ground support missions in the hills beyond the Leyte beaches. The crew of St. Lo hoped and prayed that their deck would still be intact to retrieve her aircraft. But, even if the deck was operable, the St. Lo crew wondered if they would really hold a course into the wind to take on aircraft. Such a maneuver, leaving the CVE in a near standstill position, might allow the big Japanese warships to blow her out of the water.

Aboard White Plains, the crew felt the same fears as those aboard St. Lo. "Lucky White," as her blue-jackets called White Plains, had truly been lucky during this first hour and half of battle. Since the Japanese first opened fire shortly before 0700, White Plains had yet to suffer real damage. Japanese cruisers had aimed several 8" and 6" salvos at White Plains, but, miraculously, not a single one of the 30 shells had come close to Lucky White. The shells had merely spewed geysers of water off every quarter of the jeep carrier. The crew of White Plains expected that sooner or later their CVE would start taking punishment, perhaps even lethal blows. These sailors too worried about returning airmen. Their aircraft had left the deck at 0600 hours this morning to make long range support strikes on Leyte. Surely, the

173

aircraft would be out of ammo, bombs, and even fuel by the time they returned to the carrier.

Finally, aboard Fanshaw Bay, Admiral Clifton Ziggy Sprague appeared astonishingly calm, despite the damage and fire on the jeep carrier. The worry wart of 50 years had now apparently resigned himself to the inevitable. He had done all he could to lead the jeep carriers in a zigzagging run to avoid the Japanese warships and to keep the enemy surface fleet away from Leyte Gulf. But now, he was quite convinced the Japanese would finish off Taffy 3 before the morning ended. Still, the longer he lured the Japanese into chasing his carriers, the longer he delayed the Japanese from entering Leyte Gulf to carry out an awesome massacre. If Sprague retarded the Japanese long enough, perhaps the battleships and cruisers of 7th fleet or mass air formations from the 3rd Fast Carrier Fleet might yet save the ships in San Pedro Bay and the GI's on the Leyte beaches.

Fanshaw Bay had certainly taken her share of hits, although only three men had been killed and twenty more wounded. Unfortunately, two of the hits had ripped up the flight deck, always a primary target for Japanese gunners. And now, at 0830 hours, the Taffy 3 commander watched anxiously as repair crews worked furiously to mend the small flight deck. Meanwhile, Sprague too scanned the skies for returning planes. Where would aircraft from the Taffy 3 escort carriers find a place to land when they returned from their air sorties against the Japanese battleships and cruisers? Cmdr. Bob Roberts had been out with a half dozen Corsairs and a half dozen

Avengers of Composite Squadron 68. But worse, another dozen of Fanshaw Bay's aircraft had been out since 0530 hours on CAP and antisubmarine patrols. They would be returning within the next hour. Could the work crews repair Fanshaw Bay's deck to retrieve these 24 aircraft?

Ziggy Sprague drank coffee on the bridge of the Taffy 3 flagship that now tilted and weaved as the helmsman veered and swung the carrier erratically to avoid further Japanese shells. Sprague looked at Captain Carsen, his chief of staff, who had again raised both Admiral Halsey and Admiral Kinkaid.

"Well? What do they say?"

"Same thing, Sir," Carsen answered. "Admiral Kinkaid's battleships are still at full ahead and they expect to be here in two hours."

"Two hours!" Sprague huffed. "Christ, we can't hold off that long. We'll all be at the bottom by then." He took a quick gulp of his coffee and then looked at Carsen again. "What about Halsey?"

"The four carriers and two battleships he's sending down to help us are also at full ahead. But, it'll still be three hours before the carriers can start launching air strikes."

"Goddamn," Sprague cursed again. "Nothing'll be afloat by then, not us, and not those ships in San Pedro Bay."

"No, Sir," Captain Carsen answered.

"What's going on ashore?"

"Confusion and panic, Sir," Captain Carsen said. "General MacArthur is infuriated. He's been cursing the navy ever since this thing started. We're told he's got every man ashore packing up to evacuate into the hills. We've heard that even some of the sailors aboard auxiliary ships in the bay are heading for shore to move inland with the GI's."

"That's something, isn't it?" Ziggy Sprague scowled. "Those guys in the hills fighting the Nips are safer than our sailors in San Pedro Bay." He paused again and once more scanned the empty skies. "I'm worried about our planes. Where the hell will they land with most of our flight decks chopped to pieces?"

"I don't know, Sir."

Admiral Sprague sighed. "Okay." He turned to Captain Johnson. "Continue evasive action and let's hope for the best."

"Yes, Sir," the Fanshaw Bay skipper answered. But there was no life in his voice. He had apparently lost the optimism he had only a few minutes ago.

Like Sprague and the hundreds of other sailors in Taffy 3, Johnson now felt a sense of frustrating helplessness. There was no place to run, no place to hide, and no chance to avoid for much longer the 8", 14" and 18" shells from the Japanese cruisers and destroyers. And further, sooner or later, the Japanese Desron columns would launch torpedoes at them. At their 25 to 30 knot speed, the enemy ships would soon be within point blank range. Even at full ahead the CVE's could make no more than 17 knots. Now, Captain Johnson scanned the skies, but he saw no planes. He sighed in resignation. What difference did it make? They were all going to the bottom anyway.

Then, at 0833, the roar of planes. Four air units from Taffy 3 were on the way back: Cmdr. Bob

Roberts with five Avengers and five Corsairs from Fanshaw Bay, the ten survivors of the attacks on the Japanese ships; Cmdr. Ed Huxtable with six Dauntlesses and eight Hellcats from Gambier Bay's Composite 10 Squadron, all that had escaped Japanese anti-aircraft guns; Cmdr. Bill Keighley of Kalinin Bay with his ten Hellcats and six Avengers, survivors of Composite Squadron 3; and Cmdr. Bob Fowler returning with his remaining ten Hellcats and fourteen Avengers from Kitkun Bay's Composite Squadron 5.

Now, at 0833 hours, Cmdr. Bob Roberts radioed Fanshaw Bay. "We're coming in. Please prepare to retrieve aircraft."

"We've got a couple of holes in the deck, Sir," the radioman said, "but they've got one of them patched. You'll have to come in cautiously, and you'd better get in quick before some more of those Japanese shells tear up more of our flight deck."

"Roger," the 68th Composite Squadron commander answered before he headed swiftly towards Fanshaw Bay with his five Avengers and five Corsairs.

At the same 0833 hours, Cmdr. Ed Huxtable tried to call Gambier Bay. "Dexter 10, Dexter 10; this is Dexter 10A. Come in, please; come in."

But, Huxtable got no response.

The Composite Squadron 10 commander called again. "Dexter 10, do you read me? Come in. Come in."

But still no answer. How could Huxtable know that his Gambier Bay was beginning to settle under the blue waters of the Philippine Sea? How could he guess that no one from the CVE, including Captain

Viewig, was any longer aboard the battered, smoking, shattered Gambier Bay?

In the lead Dauntless of Composite Squadron 3, Cmdr. Bill Keighley called Kalinin Bay. "Catnip 3; Catnip 3; this is Catnip 3A. Come in."

"We read you," the radio operator of Kalinin Bay answered.

"We're coming in. Please prepare to retrieve aircraft. We've got six bombers and eight fighters. We lost four."

"You can't come in, Sir."

"What the hell do you mean we can't come in?" Keighley answered angrily. "We're out of ammo and low on gas. If we don't land within the next half hour, we're done. Do you expect us to fly around on empty fuel tanks?"

"The ship is in shambles, Sir," the radio operator said. "Jap shells have knocked out the flight deck and knocked out half the other compartments. We have at least a dozen fires aboard and we're trying to contain them."

"Good Christ," Keighley hissed. "What the hell are we supposed to do? Can you direct us to one of the other carriers?"

"They're just as bad off, Sir. I think you'll need to ditch in the bay. Maybe some of the auxiliary ships in San Pedro Bay can pick you up."

Cmdr. Bill Keighley closed his eyes and felt frustration race through his lean frame. The entire morning had been a disaster. They had caused only minimal damage to the Japanese ships and now he and the other pilots and crews of Composite Squadron 3 had nowhere to go—like bees trying to return to a destroyed hive.

178

Cmdr. Bob Fowler of Kitkun Bay's Composite Squadron 5 got the same unnerving answer. Fowler had taken off from Kitkun Bay with his entire complement of CVE planes—28 of them. Now, he was coming home with 24 of them. When he called the operations room of Kitkun Bay, the radio operator gave Fowler the bad news.

"We've got a lot of holes in the flight deck, Sir. Repair crews are working frantically to patch them."

"How long will it take?" Fowler asked.

'I don't know, Sir; maybe a half hour or even an hour."

"An hour," Fowler cried. "All 24 of my planes will be in the sea by then. None of us has more than a half hour gas supply. Can we go to another carrier?"

"They're just as bad off, Sir," the radio operator said, "and I don't know who can take aboard 24 aircraft. Anyway, the way those Japanese shells are hitting us, Commander, I don't know if any of these CVE's will still be afloat in a half hour."

"Goddamn it, goddamn it," Cmdr. Bob Fowler answered.

"Some of the other CVE's have told their pilots to ditch in the bay," the operator of Kitkun Bay said. "They figure with all those ships in San Pedro Bay, somebody is bound to pull them out of the water; or, maybe you can try some of the escort carriers of Taffy 2."

"Okay, okay," Fowler answered. Then, he slumped into the seat of his cockpit, utterly drained. He looked at his fuel gauge. The needle now wavered around the half mark. They were finished: the planes, the CVE'S, the Leyte beachhead.

Aboard battleship Yamato, Admiral Takeo Kurita peered from the bridge with binoculars. He could see the pall of smoke from the burning U. S. carriers far to the south. Then he scanned the broken cloud skies, empty of American aircraft now. The center force commander pursed his lips. He was about to raise his binoculars again when his aide handed him a message.

"For you, Honorable Kurita," Communications Officer Masataki Okimuya said.

The admiral read the report: "Air assaults have ended and all enemy aircraft have retired to the south."

Kurita looked at Admiral Koyanagi. "Once we have completed reformation to No. 19 battle disposition, we will continue cautiously to the south at 20 knots. We are still not certain of the enemy's strength. Meanwhile, continue fire."

"Yes, Honorable Kurita."

The 1st Striking Force commander then raised his binoculars once more to study the smoke to the south, which covered the entire horizon. His gunners had done well thus far. But then he scowled. He had still failed to make contact with Admirals Shima and Nishimura; nor had they contacted him. Kurita wondered if the 2nd Striking Force had made Surigao Strait and if they were approaching Leyte Gulf. Kurita still had no idea that Nishimura's fleet had been almost destroyed and that the surviving ships under Admiral Shima had retired to the west.

"Honorable Kurita," an aide suddenly interrupted Kurita, "would you honor us and have some tea?"

Kurita nodded, lowered his binoculars and then

sipped the tea. He then peered again from Yamato's bridge to note that his warships had again formed into No. 19 disposition: Batdiv 3 and Batdiv 1 in tandem, Desron 10 in its double column with light cruiser Yahagi in the lead, Crudiv 7 in Column, and Crudiv 2 of Haguro and Chokai in tandem. Except for cruiser Kumano, the air attacks and the tin can attacks had done little damage to Kurita's fleet. His force was still at near full strength.

Then, Communications Officer Masataki Okimuya came onto the bridge with some slips of paper in his hand. "Admiral, we bring you gratifying news. Our monitors have picked up enemy radio reports. The American air units that attacked our fleet are now in serious trouble. According to our radio listeners, our gun fire has destroyed or so badly damaged the flight decks of the enemy carriers that the Yankee aircraft have no place to land."

"Nowhere to land?"

"No, Honorable Kurita. One of the enemy carriers is already sinking and two others are perilously close to sinking. The enemy's radio operators aboard the American carriers have suggested to their airmen that they crash land in San Pedro Bay and then hope for rescue from American auxiliary ships anchored in the bay."

"Then the enemy carriers no longer have the means to launch aircraft?" Kurita asked.

"Apparently not," Cmdr. Okimuya said.

Admiral Takeo Kurita took a long sip of his tea, stared again at the smoking horizon to the south, and then turned to Admiral Koyanagi with a grin, a rare phenomenon for the perpetually sober face of the 1st Striking Force commander. "Tomiji, order full flank speed. We will complete the destruction of this enemy carrier fleet within the hour. Then we will sail into Leyte Gulf."

"Yes, Admiral," Koyanagi answered, a grin now creasing his own face.

Chapter Eleven

Ziggy Sprague felt drained. Not only was the Japanese fleet closing fast, but many of the returning Taffy 3 aircraft had no place to land. But he would take first things first—try again to stall the Japanese advance. He called on the only man he could, Captain Bill Thomas. At 0834 hours, he spoke to his screen commander.

"I know your Desron 46 had a rough time, Bill, but I've got to ask you to try again. Maybe you can slow them up again or break their battle formation again—anything."

"We'll do what we can, Sir," Captain Thomas answered.

Aboard USS Johnson, medics had stopped the bleeding and bandaged Cmdr. Evans' hand where he had lost two fingers. When Evans got the call from Captain Thomas, the GQ Johnny commander never winced. His guns were now under manual control, but repair crews had repaired engines to increase speed to 20 knots. Evans, peering through binoculars, spotted light cruiser Yahagi and her seven destroyers of Desron 10. The Japanese column was moving into position to finally launch its torpedoes at the fleeing Taffy 3 jeep carriers.

At 0835, the crews on both Hoel and Samuel Roberts were making repairs, while Heermann and John Butler were trying to make smoke. The other DDE's, Dennis and Raymond, were scooting to take on Gambier Bay's survivors. But, with the new order from Captain Bill Thomas, the two destroyer escorts once more veered north, with USS Johnson plying recklessly into the lead.

Aboard Yahagi, Admiral Susumu Kimura had been peering through binoculars at the fleeing, zig-zagging escort carriers when he suddenly saw Johnson come out of a smoke screen and head straight towards his light cruiser. "The fool is mad! Mad! He barely survived the last attack. Does this foolish destroyer commander expect to be so fortunate again?"

"He is foolish indeed," answered Captain Masi Yoshimura, Yahagi's skipper. Then Yoshimura called his gunnery officer, Commander Tadashi Otani. "Open fire on the Yankee destroyer at once."

"Yes, Captain," Otani cried.

But, before the Japanese gunners swung their 6" turret, Johnson unleashed a salvo of 5" shells and then launched a torpedo attack. The twin assault forced the helmsman of Yahagi to swing out of column, executing a right rudder, to avoid the torpedoes from the American destroyer. Both Kimura and Yoshimura reddened in anger, and the Desron 10 commander picked up his radio phone to call his destroyer commanders.

"Attack the brazen Yankee destroyer at once! At once!"

184

Aboard Johnson, Cmdr. Evans continued his reckless plunge towards Yahagi, firing 5" guns in rapid salvos. He had closed range to 5,000 yards when two of GQ Johnny's 5" shells struck Yahagi's starboard aft, knocking out a storage compartment and a 20MM gunpit. Then, in rapid succession, Johnson scored several more hits on Yahagi. The light cruiser veered 90 degrees and broke off action to excape the astonishing fire from Johnson.

Kimura was furious and cried again into his radio phone. "With all speed, you must deal with this brazen American vessel," he told his destroyer commanders.

The destroyers of Desron 10 responded. Soon, salvos of 5" shells from the seven destroyers sailed from every direction towards already badly damaged USS Johnson. The American destroyer caught several hits, but none were fatal. Evans shifted gunfire to Desron 10's destroyer Nowaki. The Johnson gunners scored two hits and Nowaki also veered out of column. The other destroyers of Desron 10 launched torpedoes at the spunky American destroyer, but all missed. Then, as Johnson came within 4,000 yards of the destroyer, Cmdr. Evans was astonished to see the next Japanese reaction. The remaining enemy destroyers turned 90 degrees and opened range on the American destroyer.

Then, remarkably, the scattered destroyers of Desron 10 launched torpedoes at the jeep carriers of Taffy 3. Since the battle started, Desron 10's principal goal was to get in a devastating torpedo attack on the baby flat tops. But the destroyers could not have launched torpedoes at a worse time:

they were scattered and the jeep carriers were too far away. None of the Japanese torpedoes hit anything, and in fact some did not even reach the American escort carriers.

Thus, one damaged destroyer, USS Johnson, her own torpedoes expended, one engine lost, and considerably damaged, had managed to disconcert a Japanese destroyer column. After the war, Admiral Kurita admitted that the brazen little American destroyer had foiled the plans of Desron 10 to make a telling torpedo launch on the escort carriers of Taffy 3.

As the Japanese destroyers wildly launched their torpedoes at the baby flat tops, Evans, on the bridge of Johnson, could not restrain his elation.

"Goddamn, now I've seen everything."

But, Cherokee Evans would pay for his brazen action. The enemy destroyers came quickly about after Admiral Kimura berated the commanders over his radio phone. "Are you utter fools? Do we have idiots in command of our vessels? Resume attack! Resume attack at once on the American destroyer. Obliterate her so we can once more launch torpedoes at the American carriers."

On the deck of Johnson, both Lt. Bob Hagen and Chief Jim O'Gerek stiffened when they saw the enemy destroyers reform and speed towards GQ Johnny, a culprit that had made the skippers of these Japanese destroyers lose face with their Desron 10 commander.

"Jesus Christ, Sir," O'Gerek hissed, "they're coming back at us."

"We've still got some fighting to do, Chief," Lt. Hagen answered.

"With what?" O'Gerek asked. "We've expended torpedoes and we haven't got a dozen shells left."

Lt. Hagen called the bridge. "Captain," he said to Cmdr. Evans, "trouble. We're about out of ammo and those Nips are closing fast. You better order smoke and get us the hell out of here. We can't do any more."

"Okay," Evans answered.

At 0849, before smoke screen, Johnson and her crew found themselves in a position, however, where all the guts in the world would do them no good.

While several destroyers from Desron 10 closed on Johnson, the cruisers of Crudiv 7 closed from the port side. A skyful of 8" and 5" shells began pelting USS Johnson. The first hit knocked out the forward gun, damaged another gun, and started fires. More exploding shells knocked out the 40MM locker room and caused more damage. Next, a staccato of exploding 5 inchers tore apart the already damaged bridge, killing all in there, except Evans and the helmsman. In a dazed and injured state, Evans managed to pick up his JV and shift command to the fantail.

The harassed gunners aboard Johnson desperately traded shots with the enemy, first against the destroyers and then against the cruisers. But they had limited ammunition and every man aboard GQ Johnny suspected that they were finished.

Soon, another avalanche of shells knocked out completely the starboard engine room and another shell knocked out the nearly repaired director to end completely all power and communications. The next rain of shells shattered the remaining guns aboard Johnson—except for #4 turret gun that continued to lob intermittent shells by local control. Then, as fires erupted throughout the ship, Evans screamed into his JV.

"Scuttle all depth charges, scuttle all depth charges!"

Evans did not want his ship blown apart from internal explosions.

Now, GQ Johnny slapped across the sea as best she could on one engine, while the helmsman zigzagged, spraying huge crests from the bow. But the destroyer had only made another few knots when a new Japanese 8 incher struck behind the bridge. The explosion tore a bulkhead away and sprayed the bridge house with fire, shrapnel and metal. The hit left the bridge officer dead in a contorted heap under twisted metal and wreckage. The helmsman lay across his wheel, his punctured body spurting blood and his head bashed beyond recognition. Cherokee Evans miraculously survived the explosion and he rose dizzily to his feet to crawl toward a JV. "Corpsmen! Corpsmen! Up on the bridge!"

Within moments, two medics and Lt. Bob Hagen had pushed their way into the damaged bridge house. The corpsmen could do nothing for the others here, but they worked furiously on Cmdr. Ernie Evans, while Hagen ordered another helmsman to the wheelhouse. Even as the corpsmen bandaged new lacerations on Cherokee Evans' barrel shaped body, Evans looked at Lt. Hagen.

"How bad are we, Bob?"

"Bad, Ernie, bad," Hagen answered. "We're making repairs and putting out fires as fast as we can, but I don't know. We've got manual control on our last gun, #4, but we'll be firing our last shot pretty soon. Our speed is down to ten knots, without one engine, and with flooding and list."

Evans squeezed his face. Then he looked at the new helmsman who arrived on the bridge. "Steer a southwest course."

"Aye, Sir."

But the cascade of Japanese shellfire continued to rain on USS Johnson, until one hit knocked out the #2 engine room. The American destroyer slid to a near stop as the speedy Japanese ships closed on her. By 0852, the ship was aflame from bow to stern and dead in the water. Then Evans issued the order:

"Abandon ship! Abandon ship!"

GQ Johnny's bluejackets scrambled over the side, tossing rafts into the choppy water of the Philippine Sea ahead of them. As the men abandoned, taking wounded with them, the Japanese Desron 10 column closed around burning Johnson like Indians attacking a prairie schooner. They laced the battered Johnson at point blank range, blowing her to pieces. At 0910, GQ Johnny rolled over and sank.

From her complement of 327 men, only 141 survived. Of the 186 men afloat, 45 would die from injuries before rescue, including Cmdr. Ernie Cherokee Evans. Cmdr. Evans had been seen in the water for a few minutes after abandon ship, but he was never seen again. Both Lt. Hagen and Chief O'Gerek would be among the rescued survivors of USS Johnson.

There seems little question that GQ Johnny's efforts had broken up both the Crudiv 7 and Desron 10 battle lines before these two Japanese fleet divisions could finish off the jeep carriers of Taffy 3 with shellfire and torpedoes. Not only Kumano earlier, but cruisers Chokai and Chikuma had also been hit by Johnson torpedoes in this second Johnson attack. While the torpedoes had caused minimal damage to these two heavy cruisers, the hits had forced both vessels to slow up and make repairs.

Little Samuel Roberts had again followed USS Johnson into the fray. At 0834 hours, even as repair crews worked on the DDE, Lt. Cmdr. Bob Copeland trailed USS Johnson at 3,000 yards astern. The Samuel Roberts commander peered through his binoculars at the steaming Japanese cruisers to the northwest and the steaming Desron 10 to the northeast. When Johnson veered right after Desron 10, Copeland ordered a ten degree port turn to once more take on the Japanese cruisers of Crudiv 7. When he came within 7,000 yards, Copeland called his torpedo officer.

"Ready torpedo launch."

"Torpedo launch ready, Sir," the torpedo officer answered.

However, before Cmdr. Copeland could order launch, an 8" shell hit Samuel Roberts squarely on the starboard quarter below the waterline and knocked out the #1 fire room. As repair crews worked desperately to seal flooding, another 8" shell hit the radio antenna that toppled down and hit the torpedo tubes, dislodging the speed setting wrench. A torpedo launch was now out of the question.

"Reduce speed, reduce speed!" Copeland cried, "and turn turret guns on that cruiser."

When the helmsman slowed, the Samuel Roberts gunners spun their turrets and sent 3" and 4" shells at cruiser Tone, 3rd in the Crudiv line. Flames and smoke erupted from the cruiser's stern, prompting the cruiser to fall out of column. The men aboard USS Samuel Roberts cheered, encouraged, and her gunners sent another salvo after the Japanese cruiser.

However, the gunners aboard Tone, incensed by the fire from Samuel Roberts, soon enough unleashed their own salvos at the little wolf, even as the Japanese cruiser increased speed and plowed swiftly towards Samuel Roberts, coming within 5,000 yards of the American tin can. Tone then sent another 8" salvo at the DDE. The helmsman on Samuel Roberts, slowed, sped up, turned, or fishtailed in an attempt to avoid the rain of shellfire. In its frantic maneuvers, Samuel Roberts almost ran into Destroyer Heermann that was speeding north to attack the Japanese battleships.

The men aboard Samuel Roberts sighed in relief when they luckily missed a collision with the Desron 46 flagship. But, as Samuel Roberts turned away, she caught a powerful 14" hit, probably from battleship Kongo. The huge explosion hit the superstructure deck house and completely obliterated the house, a 40MM gun mount and the after 40MM Mark 51 director. No trace of the mounts, guns, shields, or gun crews was ever seen. The hit abruptly slowed Samuel Roberts to 17 knots.

Then, at 0845 hours, another tandem pair of 14" shells, also from Kongo, exploded on the DDE in tremendous explosions. The hits tore a 30 foot hole on the port side, wiped out the #2 engine room, ruptured fuel tanks, and started fires on the fantail. The stack disintegrated into nothing more than masses of twisted metal. Macerated dead and moaning wounded lay throughout the battered ship. Samuel Roberts lost all power and all capacity to move. She no longer had either offensive or defensive measures to protect herself.

"Abandon ship! Abandon ship!" Lt. Cmdr. Bob Copeland cried from the battered bridge. Samuel Roberts was going down and Copeland knew his ship would surely be hit again, and the next 14" hit would chop the small DDE into fragments.

Even as USS Johnson started down, the men aboard Samuel Roberts hastily threw rafts over the side, helped wounded into the rafts, and then jumped into the choppy waters themselves. The survivors had barely left the DDE before an internal explosion blew a huge hole in the starboard quarter and sea water poured into the vessel in huge torrents, rapidly listing the shattered ship to 80 degrees.

The survivors, floundering on the sea, now saw heavy cruiser Tone loom out of the north and plow past them, sending up huge waves. The American sailors held their breath in terror, expecting a chatter of cruiser machine gun fire to cut them to pieces on the choppy surface of the Philippine Sea. However, Tone's sailors merely leaned over the port railings and took pictures of the floundering sailors and the listing, flaming USS Samuel Roberts.

By the time Tone had moved past the shipless American sailors, the fatally hit Samuel Roberts rolled over on her port beam. At 0905 hours, the DDE gave a final twist and then sank, stern first.

Of her crew of 8 officers and 170 men, three officers and 86 sailors died from hits on the ship or died in the rafts during the long wait for rescue.

Still, the efforts by the small USS Samuel Roberts had also helped the harried American jeep carriers to gain another respite before aircraft came once more to hit the Japanese fleet.

Meanwhile, the other vessels of Desron 46 also took on the huge 1st Striking Force. Destroyer Hoel, damaged and slowed by earlier hits from battleship Kongo and cruiser Haguro, again plowed towards the Japanese battleships. From Hoel's bridge, Cmdr. Larry Kintberger stared anxiously as exploding shells erupted around his ship. Still, he plowed on recklessly and finally cried into his JV.

"Launch torpedoes!"

One spread headed straight for Kongo, and the big battleship veered to avoid it. Then, Kongo steamed northwest along the track of the torpedoes, all but taking the huge warship out of the fight. The second Hoel torpedo spread headed for heavy cruiser Haguro of Crudiv 5. One of the fish struck the fantail of Haguro, shuddering the vessel and slowing her down, the second time Hoel had so punished her.

Hoel's crew cheered in satisfaction. They had disrupted both a battleship and a heavy cruiser. But they soon paid dearly for their audacity. A moment later, a 14" shell, probably from Batdiv 3" Haruna, shuddered Hoel as the hit almost tore away the stern. A moment later, another 14 incher struck aft, blowing away the turret gun and wrecking the electrical system. These new hits, coupled with the earlier hits on the first attack, were enough for

Kintberger. He called for a quick retirement, turning the vessel with hand steering and plugging south on one engine. As Hoel retreated, her gunners sent another salvo of 5 inchers at Crudiv 5 and one shell knocked out Haguro's antenna, forcing the heavy cruiser to veer erratically to the east.

However, more 8" and 14" shells followed in Hoel's wake and Cmdr. Kintberger frantically called the engine room. "Can you make more speed?"

"No, Sir, we've got her as fast as possible. We're trying to make repairs on the #2 port engine, but I don't think we can."

"Keep trying," Kintberger said.

"Aye, Sir."

But Japanese ships were now closing on Hoel, boxing her in. Thus far, Japanese gunners had sent nearly 200 three and two gun salvos towards damaged USS Hoel. Kintberger had watched these geysers fearfully, while he had maneuvered his ship into the recent splashes, just as Gellhorn had done aboard Gambier Bay, on the theory that Japanese salvos would not hit the same place twice. Unfortunately, Kintberger found himself in the same trouble as Gellhorn. He simply could not chase salvos indefinitely because too many shells were bursting around the U. S. destroyer. Hoel could barely turn because of her jammed rudder and she had little speed now because of a damaged bow, a list from flooding, and a dead engine.

The Japanese battleship Kongo soon came within 8,000 yards of Hoel's damaged stern and the two cruisers of Crudiv 2, Chokai and troubled Haguro, were a mere 7,000 yards off Hoel's starboard quarter.

The array of hits so far had left the American destroyer with only two guns in operable condition, and these were on the forward, making all but impossible the task of firing back. Further, Hoel had expanded all torpedoes.

Then, at 0900 hours, another solid hit struck Hoel and knocked out the starboard engine room. The U. S. destroyer thus lost all power.

Now, dead in the water, Hoel suffered a rain of hits. Ironically, the big 14" shells went right through the ship and out the other side without exploding because of the close range. The smaller shells, the 5 and 6 inchers from the cruiser secondary batteries, caused the real damage. Many of the shells were antipersonnel shells that caused extensive casualties when they exploded. Other shells, incendiaries, ignited fires on the American destroyer. Finally, two 8" shells opened a huge hole on Hoel's starboard to start uncontrolled flooding and quicken Hoel's list to 20 degrees.

"We're done, Sir, we're done," Lt. Green said.

Cmdr. Kintberger nodded. "We'll have to abandon."

"Aye, Sir," Green answered.

At 0905, survivors from Hoel threw rafts over the side, lowered wounded, and then spilled over the sides themselves. But, even as the men abandoned ship, the Japanese raked the doomed tin can with more shells, killing many of the bluejackets clambering off the ship or jumping into the water. The staccato of shells literally tore Hoel apart and at 0921, the American destroyer simply rolled over and sank, stern first.

Lt. Green, foundering, found a raft where he joined Cmdr. Larry Kintberger, the Hoel commander, who was quite hurt. They and other survivors would wallow in the sea for 48 hours before rescue by LCI. Of the Hoel's crew, 252 men would be dead or missing. Among the 82 survivors would be Lt. Green and Cmdr. Kintberger.

Destroyer Heermann, meanwhile, had come full steam northeast and almost ran into jeep carrier Fanshaw Bay that had taken a lacing from Japanese gunfire. But the destroyer veered and narrowly missed a collision before Heermann continued on.

"I don't like this," Lt. Bob Newcombe, the deck officer, told Cmdr. Al Hathaway. "They almost got us the last time."

"Somebody's got to stop those goddamn enemy ships," Hathaway said. "They've already got Gambier Bay and they may get Kalinin Bay and Fanshaw Bay. We'll try to get close enough to launch a torpedo spread."

"Aye, Sir," Newcombe answered.

At 0841, cruisers Tone and Chikuma acknowledged brazen Heermann by shifting secondary batteries on the destroyer as they had already trained main batteries on Fanshaw Bay. During the next two minutes, Japanese shells walked on Heermann, starting from 1,000 yards down to 100 yards—and then a direct hit on Heermann's bridge. The explosion killed three men, including the helmsman. This had been the second hit on the bridge today. Luckily, Cmdr. Hathaway had just left the bridge for the fire control tower to observe enemy shelling and had thus avoided death. Lt. Bob Newcombe suffered sev-

196

eral gashes from flying shrapnel, but he quickly took over the helm. He lead Heermann right through a gauntlet of Japanese fire to within 5,000 yards of Batdiv 1 where Newcombe ordered open fire with 5" guns until they could get into position for a torpedo launch.

But shells began straddling Heermann with increased rapidity and accuracy. One shell hit the uptake and another shell hit the No. 2 gun mount. A third 8 incher struck the sound dome, while the next hit tore a five foot hole in Frame #18 of the port hull below the platform deck. Another hit blew away Frame #19 on starboard. The hits quickly started flooding in A-5 and A-4 compartments. Hits also struck topside, wrecking the sound gear, pit log, SG radar, and transmitter. By 0905, Heermann's superstructure was shattered in a dozen places. But still the shells came. Two 8 inchers blew away both the aft and midship torpedo pads, ruling out any chance to launch torpedoes.

By 0907 hours, the forward area of Heermann was flooded, bow down, and Heermann could not make speed or maneuverability. The American destroyer had been as terribly unlucky this time as she had been gratefully lucky the first time she came after the big Japanese battleship.

From the bridge of battleship Nagato, Admiral Yusi Kobe peered at the hard pressed Heermann and ordered more salvos on the American destroyer from secondary batteries. "We must destroy the enemy destroyer before she releases a new smoke screen to hide the carriers once more from our view."

"Yes, Honorable Kobe," the Nagato executive officer said.

But Heermann, however battered, managed to lay a smoke screen before Nagato's gunners could fire again. The American tin can not only hid herself, but once more hid the harried Fanshaw Bay.

The two other DDE's, Dennis and John Butler, took after Desron 10, where Johnson had left off. Gunners aboard Dennis sent a salvo of 4" shells towards light cruiser Yahagi, irking Admiral Susumu Kimura still again. His Desron 10 had already been frustrated twice by the pesky Desron 46, especially Johnson. The Japanese destroyer division had also been rattled several times by the mild air attacks. And now, another small American ship dared to interfere with the column.

To worsen Kimura's irritation, one of the 4 inchers from Dennis struck the forward #2 gun mount of the Japanese light cruiser, knocking both barrels out of commission. The Desron 10 commander reddened in fury. "Blow her out of the water! Blow the Yankee dog away!" he cried angrily into his inter-radio phone.

The Desron 10's destroyer commanders acted immediately, closing fast and sending heavy salvos of 5" shellfire on the American little wolf. One 5 incher hit Dennis's platform deck on the starboard side just above the waterline, snuffing out the lives of a deck crew. Then, an array of shell fragments put four holes in the hull above the waterline on frame #35. Another 5" hit wiped away the after 40MM director, killing two men. The next salvo, 6 inchers from Yahagi, knocked out a gun mount, the

198

automatic gun control, and the sound dome. Then, when a hit blew away frame 139 and started flooding, the Dennis skipper, Lt. Cmdr. Sam Hensen, ordered all documents thrown overboard into weighted sacks. He was now sure his little DDE would go down from enemy shellfire.

Finally, aboard DDE John Butler, Lt. Cmdr. Joe Pace, the little wolf skipper, had charged right behind Dennis, with DDE Raymond in Butler's wake. However, because of heavy Japanese gunfire, Admiral Sprague had recalled both Butler and Raymond to lay a new smoke screen around the jeep carriers.

But, by 0910, before the DDE's could lay smoke, both the cruisers of Crudiv 7 and the ships of Desron 10 had once again reformed battle order to close still again on the harried escort carriers of Taffy 3. Even the big battleships of Batdiv 1 and Batdiv 3 had straightened to come back into tandem battle order.

The Japanese sailors were angry. Admiral Kurita, Admiral Kimura, Admiral Shiraishi, and a host of other Japanese 1st Striking Force officers had reached the end of their patience. They had chased the Taffy 3 carriers for two hours but had made only 30 miles and had sunk only one carrier, Gambier Bay. By now, 1st Striking Force should have sent all six carriers to the bottom and the Japanese fleet should have been entering Leyte Gulf and heading for their shoot-fish-in-the-barrel exercise against the hundreds of American auxiliary ships in San Pedro Bay. But, the nearest ship to Leyte Gulf was DD Isokaze, and she was still 20 miles from the gulf's entrance—nearly an hour away.

However, at 0910 hours, the situation looked good

for the Japanese. Gallant Desron 46 had lost two destroyers and a DDE and the other tin cans were no longer in condition to challenge the 1st Striking Force. Further, the skies had been cleared of American aircraft for nearly an hour.

"Full ahead!" Kurita cried into his inter-radio phone again. "We have lost enough time."

From the decks of the Taffy 3 carriers and the Desron 46 tin cans still afloat, the bluejackets once more saw Crudiv 7 and Desron 10 reforming to close fast. And soon, even the big guns of the Japanese battleships loomed over the northern horizon. Not a U. S. sailor doubted that time had run out for Ziggy Sprague's little escort carrier group.

But, strangely, help would be on the way from the U. S. Army in Tacloban, on the island of Leyte.

Chapter Twelve

Before the Desron 46 tin cans had made their second attack on the Japanese fleet, Major Richard Davidson, Captain Brad Whitemore, Lt. Edward Worrad, and Lt. Russell Forrester, the navy liaison officer, had been listening to the TBS squawk among the navy ships of Taffy 3 and the airborne navy pilots of Taffy 3. At 0825, these men on Leyte heard the jeep carrier radio men tell their pilots: "No place to land on your carrier; you'll need to ditch."

"Goddamn," Davidson said, " those planes are in trouble."

"Yeah," Lt. Worrad answered. "The poor bastards have to plop in San Pedro Bay."

Only a minute later, an aggregation of planes were circling over the Calaison Peninsula. Both the soldiers on the island and the sailors aboard ships in the bay thought the planes were Japanese. Ackack guns from both San Pedro Bay and Leyte Island opened up on the planes until Lt. Forrester recognized the planes as Hellcats and Avengers. Forrester quickly called both 7th Fleet and 6th Army headquarters to halt the ack-ack fire. When the anti-aircraft fire ceased, Lt. Forrester sighed in relief, but Lt. Ed Worrad frowned.

"Goddamnit," Worrad said, "those planes are looking for someplace to land. They're birds looking for a nest."

Before anyone else spoke, one of the navy planes simply came down and alighted on the partially completed Tacloban runway. However, the aircraft churned through the soft surface, spun, and slid off the runway to sink in the mire beyond the strip.

Forrester turned to Major Davidson. "We've got to help them, Major."

Lt. Worrad's eyes brightened. "Major, we can land them, re-arm them, refuel them, and then send them out again."

"You're crazy," Davidson said.

But Worrad turned to Sgt. Sam Halpern, the grizzly ordnance chief of the 305th. "What do you think, Sergeant?"

Halpern rubbed his big face and then nodded. "Lieutenant, you get them planes down here and me and my boys will reload and refuel them. But then," he pointed, "you'll have to get 'em airborne again."

"Well?" Worrad looked at Davidson.

The 305th Airdrome Engineer commander shook his head. "We don't know a damn thing about directing or servicing navy planes."

"I do," Lt. Forrester grinned, "and I know somebody else who does."

"Who?"

"General Mitchell," the liaison officer said. "He'll help out; I know he will."

Davidson nodded and then spoke to General Ralph Mitchell, the commander of the 1st Marine Air Group Wing. "General, Sir, we want to bring in those wayward navy planes to refuel and re-arm them so they can go out again after that Japanese fleet. You must know, Sir, that most of the Taffy 3 carriers can't take them aboard because of damage. But," Davidson shook his head, "we don't know a goddamn thing about landing navy planes. Can you help out?"

"How many planes are there?" Mitchell asked.

"We don't know," Davidson answered, "but at least 40 or 50 of them. If we get them down here, we're sure we can ready them and get them off again. We'll send bomb hoists with bombs, ammo carriers with strafing belts, and fuel trucks with plenty of gas to the revetment areas."

"Son of a bitch," Mitchell grinned, "that's the best thing I've heard all day. Give me a couple of signal flags, show me where you want those planes to land, and I'll flag them in."

"I figure to land them on the old, hardpacked Japanese strip," Davidson said. "It's narrow but pretty solid. Then, when we've reloaded them, we'll send them off from the new strip. We'll have rollers keeping the strip packed down so the planes can get off."

"Good," Mitchell nodded.

"Only one thing," Davidson said, "we'll need to convince Admiral Sprague."

"I'll talk to him," Mitchell said. The marine

general first sent one of his aides to the partially completed Tacloban airfield control tower to work with the army air force sergeant there. Then, the marine general called the Taffy 3 commander. "Admiral, this is General Mitchell of the 1st Marine Wing at Tacloban. We'd like to bring in your air- craft to fuel and load so they can hit that Japanese fleet again. We'll use the old sod strip for touch- down, then service the planes, and then send them off from the new runway. I'll personally flag direct the planes. Give us ten minutes."

"You're crazy, General," Ziggy Sprague said. "I've already got some of the 5th Composite Squad- ron aircraft going to CVE Manila Bay of Taffy 2. I'm trying to find decks to retrieve some of the other Taffy 3 aircraft."

"You know goddamn well you won't find any, Admiral," Mitchell said. "Your pilots are circling around Tacloban like a flock of lost birds. The 305th Army Airdrome Engineers are setting things up and we'll have a couple of radio men direct the planes in. They can do it, Admiral, I know they can."

"I don't know," Sprague said, wavering.

"Admiral," General Mitchell persisted, "just look around you. Where can those planes go besides ditch in the bay? What have you got to lose?"

When another concussion of exploding shells from Japanese naval guns sent new geysers around Fanshaw Bay, Ziggy Sprague winced and then an- swered Mitchell over the TBS. "You're right, General, we haven't got a goddamn thing to lose." Then Sprague personally called his squadron leaders and gave them the word:

"All aircraft commanders, this is the admiral; now hear this: if you have not already alighted on a carrier deck, you are to proceed to Tacloban; proceed to Tacloban to refuel and re-arm for continued attack on the enemy fleet. Repeat: all aircraft commanders who have not alighted on carrier decks will proceed at once to Tacloban to reload and refuel for continued attack on enemy fleet. Signal crews will bring you in. Keep a watch for signal crews."

Many of the Taffy 3 pilots had already toyed with the idea of making emergency landings at Tacloban or Dulag and one had already tried it. But—re-arm and reload at an army facility? The navy to become a ward of the army?

From his Hellcat cockpit, Lt. Pat Capano called Cmdr. Bill Keighley. "Commander, did I hear right? They want us to reload and re-arm at Tacloban?"

"That's the word," Keighley answered.

"Christ, they're nuts. I can understand an emergency landing there, but how the hell can the army service us?"

"Maybe better than our own guys," Keighley said. "I heard those army guys have big 500 pound SAP's on Leyte. Anyway, it beats ditching in San Pedro Bay."

"Okay," Pat Capano sighed. "You lead, the rest of us will follow."

From Composite Squadron 10, Lt. Bob Roby called Ed Huxtable. "I don't get it, Commander. Are they crazy? Do they really expect us to bomb up at Leyte? Jesus, we'll be lucky if we can land there, much less reload and fly out again. Those army guys don't know the first thing about navy planes."

"Bobby," Huxtable answered. "You just supervise those army guys and make sure they bomb you up properly."

"This is insane," Roby persisted. "Why can't we land on some other carrier like some of those guys from 5th Squadron did?"

"Because there's no other carrier to take us. Quit arguing and follow me. We'll circle Tacloban and wait for those signal flags to lead us in."

"Yes, Sir."

Meanwhile, both Lt. Russell Forrester and Lt. Ed Worrad had set themselves up in jeeps near the Tacloban runways to work with the navy airmen overhead. Forrester would act as fleet control and Worrad would direct the planes down. Sgt. Halpern would have his ordnance crews ready to taxi the planes to revetment areas to hastily re-arm and refuel the aircraft."

Lt. Russell Forrester soon spoke to Cmdr. Bill Keighley of Composite Squadron 3 on the radio. "Commander, this is Base Forrester."

"Base Forrester? What the hell is that?"

"Your new base at Tacloban. Set your formations for deck landings and just follow instructions. You'll see the flag director to set you down."

"Roger," Cmdr. Keighley said.

Thus began the strangest partnership of World War II—army personnel directing the combat operations of navy planes. By 0835 hours, the first of the navy planes, six Avengers and eight Hellcats from

206

Kalinin Bay under Bill Keighley arched towards the old, hard packed, but narrow Japanese airstrip. Cmdr. Keighley saw the array of vehicles in the revetment areas just north of the runways: fuel trucks, tractors, bomb loaded hoist trailers, ordnance weapons carriers with crates of strafing belts, and mechanic trucks with their open rears and loaded with tools, electrical equipment, and engine supplies.

Keighley also saw the quartet of rollers on the Tacloban airstrip as the machines growled over the runway, obviously packing down the dirt surface so navy planes could take off. And finally, Cmdr. Keighley saw the men on the old sod airstrip, some with signal flags in their hands. General Mitchell and two men waited here with a half dozen Army Air Force men. The Squadron 3 commander gasped. Did they expect him to land his Avengers and Hellcats on that narrow length of sod? The strip did not appear wide enough for a piper cub. Keighley wondered how the Japanese ever got planes on and off the airstrip.

Then, a call came from General Ralph Mitchell, who held a portable TBS. "Okay, Commander, bring your planes down from the south. We'll signal you onto the strip and then direct you to revetment areas to bomb and gas up."

"I just hope the hell we get down there," Keighley said.

"Just follow our signals," General Mitchell answered.

Then down came the aircraft of Composite Squadron 3, six Avengers and eight Hellcats. First in was Cmdr. Bill Keighley who watched carefully as General

Mitchell directed him right or left with the signal flags until Mitchell suddenly held up both arms, indicating Keighley was on track. The Squadron 3 commander touched down quickly and applied his brakes. The Avenger squealed, emitting a grating echo across the field before army crews led the Avenger to revetment areas.

For the next few minutes the Avengers and Hellcats of Composite Squadron 3 came down on the old strip. Most of them made it, but an Avenger and a Hellcat slid off the runway. Growling tractors immediately pulled these planes out of the way lest they interfere with more descending aircraft.

As the planes lumbered to revetment areas, 5th Army Air Force personnel scrambled over them like ants smothering dead beetles. The army men worked swiftly, gassed up the aircraft, checked engines, and loaded 500 pound SAP bombs, one under each wing, with the help of navy pilots who showed them how to load such bombs on navy planes. Other ordnance men loaded .50 caliber strafing belts in the gun housings of both Avengers and Hellcats. Then the planes rolled from the revetment areas and onto the new Tacloban airstrip, three to a line. The runway felt soft, but quite smooth. On signal, Cmdr. Bill Keighley roared down the runway with his Avenger, kicking up dirt. Soon the Avengers and Hellcats of Squadron 3, 12 aircraft, were airborne and the scrub team ground crews sighed in relief.

Roller crews immediately growled their machines across the field, racing the length of the strip as fast as their turtle speed would take them. Meanwhile, the six Dauntlesses and eight Hellcats under

Cmdr. Ed Huxtable had also landed on the old strip before Sgt. Sam Halpern and his ordnance crews loaded and gassed up the navy planes. Then, Composite Squadron 10 also wheeled towards the head of the new runway. On signal, these navy planes, also loaded with 500 pound SAP bombs, shot down the runway, with spinning wheels churning globs of dirt behind them. This time one of the Dauntlesses and two of the Hellcats failed to get off. The three planes spun and bounced off the runway to the shoulders. Once more, a tractor dragged the planes swiftly off the runway.

Still, Huxtable got off with five Dauntlesses and six Hellcats, all loaded with 500 pounders.

Meanwhile, Cmdr. Bob Fowler of Kitkun Bay's Composite Squadron 5 had sought refuge for his 24 planes. He found that CVE Manila Bay of Taffy 2 could take ten of his planes so he landed 8 Avengers and 2 Hellcats here. Manila Bay would load these planes with torpedoes. Meanwhile, four other Hellcats went to Dulag. Lt. Walter Crocker led the remaining six Avengers and four Hellcats to Tacloban. At the army air force base, the improvised scrub team got Crocker landed, reloaded and refueled, and then off with only two planes disabled.

Finally, surviving Avengers and Hellcats of Taffy 1's CVE Santee and CVE Suwannee also came into Tacloban or Dulag. All total, 67 aircraft from the Taffy air units came to Tacloban, with 20 of them disabled on landing or take-off. Still, 47 planes had taken off safely with new bomb loads—500 pound SAP bombs.

By 0915, after the second disruption from Desron 46, 1st Striking Force was again reforming to as-sault once more the Taffy 3 carriers. But, at 0917, the first of 47 planes from Taffy 3 and the southern Taffy groups reached 1st Striking Force. Now the navy planes carried heavy, 500 pound SAP's that could cause plenty of damage. Cmdr. Bill Keighley, leading five Avengers and seven Hellcats headed for cruiser Chokai. The cruiser was booming heavy shellfire at the zig-zagging Fanshaw Bay and little DD Heermann that was trying to protect the jeep carrier.

Keighley picked up his TBS. "Okay, boys, in pairs, let's get that goddamn cruiser off the jeep carrier's back. Pat," he called Lt. Capano, "take your Hellcats in pairs from starboard and I'll take the port with our Avengers."

"Roger," Lt. Pat Capano answered.

As the Avengers and Hellcats arched towards Chokai from both sides, Captain Keno Ariga watched the aircraft. "Where did these aircraft come from?" the Chokai commander asked. "I understood the enemy carriers could no longer launch aircraft."

"I do not know, Captain," the bridge officer said.

"Hard left," Ariga cried to his helmsman, "we must avoid."

"Yes, Honorable Arigi," the helmsman answered.

Then Captain Arigi watched the antiaircraft guns from his cruiser send 40MM and 5" flak at the ap-proaching Avengers. One burst caught an Avenger squarely, sheering off a wing before the American plane cartwheeled and splashed into the sea. Ariga was satisfied, for he expected to deal easily with these aircraft that would probably strike with 100 pound bombs as they had done before.

But, Captain Ariga and his sailors aboard Chokai gaped in horror when the first two Avenger pilots, Keighley and his wingman, unleashed a quartet of 500 pound bombs. One of the bombs missed, but the other three struck squarely. One hit smashed through the deck to Chokai's port engine room, where a shuddering explosion knocked out the engine and killed a half dozen firemen. The next bomb hit the stack, almost blowing it into the superstructure and sending fragments of hot metal to the main deck. The third hit struck the signal house, knocking apart the compartment along with the signal officer and his staff.

Captain Keno Ariga gasped. "They are heavy bombs! Heavy bombs! Where could they get them?"

The bridge officer only shook his head, for he was as shocked as the Chokai commander.

Other Avenger pilots as well as Lt. Capano and the Hellcat pilots followed Cmdr. Keighley and from 500 feet, they sent more 500 pound SAP's into the frantically zig-zagging cruiser. But Chokai could not get away. Composite Squadron 3 pilots scored a dozen more hits. A trio of bombs struck amidship, gouging holes in the hull to start flooding. Two more bombs knocked out the radio room and observation tower. The next three hits struck astern, almost chopping away the fantail and starting more flooding. Then came three hits on the bow that shattered the deck and ruptured the #1 turret gun. Finally, one hit struck the #1 magazine storage house—a fatal strike.

The magazine ignited and Chokai gave a final, horrifying shudder before fire and smoke shot skyward to nearly a hundred feet. The heavy cruiser was finished. Japanese sailors ran frantically about the battered deck to stem total disaster. But fires and flooding were out of control as the blazing cruiser took a quick list to port.

Keighley picked up his TBS. "Goddamn, we got her this time."

"Commander," Pat Capano cried back, "let's get back to Tacloban and have those army boys take care of us again."

"My sentiments, too," Keighley said before he led his combined Avenger-Hellcat squadron roaring back to the Army Air Force base at Tacloban.

On the bridge of Chokai, Captain Keno Ariga coughed from the dense smoke. He could only give one order. "Abandon ship! Abandon ship!"

Less than half of Chokai's crew would survive when, at 0921 hours, the ship rolled over and sank. Cruiser Haguro's crews watched in horror as the sister ship of Crudiv 2 gurgled her last and then went to the bottom of the Philippine Sea. The attack on Chokai by Cmdr. Bill Keighley's 12 aircraft had lasted less than a minute. A mere five minutes later, the ship started down. Two Japanese destroyers from Desron 10 came forward to pick up Chokai survivors.

Next to feel the wrath of the revitalized aircraft from Taffy 3 was the cruiser Chikuma, the Japanese warship nearest the Taffy 3 carriers. At about 0918, Chikuma had been moving swiftly towards CVE White Plains, Lucky White, whose fortunes could soon run out. But, moments later, Chikuma herself would be a target.

"Enemy aircraft, enemy aircraft!" Chikuma's

lookout cried into a radio phone. "They are coming from the south under the clouds."

Captain Suzuki Norimitsu, Chikuma's skipper, rushed out of the wheelhouse to peer at the oncoming planes through his binoculars. Then, he cried into his own radio phone. "Antiaircraft! Commence antiaircraft fire at once!"

"Yes, Captain," the gunner officer answered. But, the heavy barrage of 40MM and 5" ack-ack fire failed to deter Cmdr. Ed Huxtable and his pilots of Composite Squadron 10. His five Dauntlesses and six Hellcats carried heavy 500 pound SAP's.

"Okay, boys, in pairs," Huxtable cried into his TBS. "Scramble!"

Once more sailors aboard a Japanese cruiser felt the impact of heavy 500 pound bombs. In low level dives, the first four planes of Composite Squadron 10 zoomed towards the cruiser, two planes from each side. Ack-ack fire knocked down one of the Dauntlesses, but not Huxtable's plane or the other two aircraft. Even as Chikuma zigzagged frantically to evade, she caught a pair of hits on port that shuddered her to a stop, and she then felt another shake as two more 500 pounders struck on the starboard midsection. Then concussioning explosions deafened the sailors aboard Chikuma before flames erupted from midship to bow. The heavy tremors knocked Captain Norimitsu and his bridge staff to the deck and when they struggled to their feet, they saw only smoke and flames. The captain then got a call from below.

"Honorable Norimitsu, fires have erupted throughout the storage rooms. We cannot control them."

"You must, you must," Captain Norimitsu cried.

But, Huxtable's airmen from Squadron 10 were not finished. They would extract vengeance for the damage to their mother ship, Kalinin Bay. Three more American planes came in from both sides, a Dauntless and two Hellcats, to unleash more 500 pounders. Four of them hit and tore away the stern in a staccato of bursts that erupted more fire and smoke. The hits also opened two holes in the aft to start flooding. The hits also knocked out the single mount machine gun pit, the 40MM antiaircraft pit, and the #3 gun turret. The stern slowly settled into the sea and the ship fell abruptly to a reduced speed of 15 knots. Finally, a couple of hits knocked out steering to leave Chikuma almost helpless.

Now came Cmdr. Bob Fowler with his ten planes that had landed on CVE Manila Bay of Taffy 2 to re-arm with torpedoes. The Hellcats first raked Chikuma's deck with .50 caliber strafing fire. Then, Bob Fowler led his Avengers towards the flaming cruiser with torpedo strikes. Two of the torpedoes scored and Chikuma vibrated fiercely. Now, with the list and with stern down, the heavy cruiser appeared finished. The American airmen could see destroyer Nowaki of Desron 10 plow towards the obviously doomed Chikuma, while DD Urakaze remained with sinking Chokai.

As heavy cruisers Chokai and Chikuma started down, the losses rattled the Japanese sailors on other ships of the 1st Striking Force. The vessels scattered out of battle formation, ignoring their

214

jeep carrier quarry, to avoid the new swarms of enemy planes. But, on came more Tacloban serviced Avengers and Hellcats. Aircraft from Composite Squadron 5 under Lt. Walter Crocker and aircraft from the southern Taffy units also singled out targets.

Crocker's half dozen Avengers and four Hellcats from Gambier Bay roared towards flaming Chikuma where DD Nowaki's antiaircraft gunners made a feeble effort to stop them. Most of the crews aboard Nowaki were so busy trying to rescue Chikuma survivors that they had little time to fight off American planes. Thus, Crocker and his airmen enjoyed a near unmolested attack.

Lt. Walter Crocker cried into his TBS. "Looks like the cruiser's finished. We'll take on that destroyer."

The Avenger and Hellcat airmen of Composite Squadron 5 now came roaring down on DD Nowaki, unleashing 500 pound SAP's. One bomb hit Nowaki's fantail and sliced away a chunk of stern, while another hit shattered the after 5" gun turret. A third hit sailed completely through the superstructure and into the engine room where the bomb exploded, knocked out #2 engine, and started flooding. A fourth 500 pounder struck the aft observation deck and blew away the deck and staff. Heavy .50 caliber strafing fire killed over a dozen men aboard Nowaki and injured dozens more.

When Crocker and his pilots left the area, Nowaki's stern was awash and her superstructure was afire. Crocker and his airmen had avenged to some extent the loss of CVE Gambier Bay.

"Okay, we're going back to Tacloban to reload,"

Crocker cried over his TBS. "On the double!"

"Aye, aye, Lieutenant," a gleeful ensign answered.

Finally, the last complement of planes from Tacloban, 20 Avengers and Hellcats from the southern Taffy units, headed for the battleships. Half of the navy planes went after battleship Kongo that had been harried all morning. Kongo had taken an array of hits, first from Taffy 3's tin cans, then from the earlier strike by Taffy 3 aircraft, and then by the Taffy 3 tin cans again.

Kongo's gunners, totally irate over the nuisance by the Americans, now sent up antiaircraft fire with a determined resolve. Within moments, four American planes went down. One blew up in mid air, another had its wings sheered off before plopping into the sea, a third trailed smoke, wobbling erratically, and then splashing into the water. The fourth plane exploded in a fire ball and dropped like a burning balloon to the surface of the sea.

Still, the southern Taffy planes came on. The big battleship soon took heavy hits. One bomb tore apart a section of the stern, two bombs struck and damaged the superstructure, a pair of 500 pounders disintegrated part of Kongo's signal house. More 500 pounders, exploding in a line of bursts on the huge foredeck, left several holes and damaged one of the guns. The big battleship raced about at top speed, zigging and zagging, while her gunners fired furiously at the darting planes, not unlike a horse trying to brush away pesky flies with its tail.

Still, the bomb hits did not materially endanger the vessel, slow her down, or reduce her speed. Repair crews worked swiftly to put out fires and

216

to clear away debris.

The other southern Taffy planes went after Nagato where SAP bombs started starboard fires on the big battleship. Ack-ack knocked down two of the planes and the battleship was not seriously damaged.

Still, the hits on the battleship had shocked Admiral Takeo Kurita. When he looked at his fleet, he saw his ships scattered again, skimming about the sea haphazardly. Further, he learned that cruisers Chokai and Chikuma were burning and sinking and that DD Nowaki was listing. Even as Kurita tried to digest these disappointments, Cmdr. Masataki Okimuya came onto the bridge with several sheafs of paper in his hand.

"Honorable Kurita," the communications officer said, "our radio operators have monitored some disturbing news. We have learned that the carrier planes have been landing at Tacloban to re-arm and refuel."

Kurita scowled. "They are following a technique begun by our own navy air units. The enemy's carrier aircraft are utilizing land bases to stage for these new air attacks." He peered through the forward window of the bridge to study the rising smoke from the sinking Gambier Bay and from the other burning American ships. "Bakarya," he cursed. "The Americans do not need their carriers."

"We have other distressing reports," Okimuya said. "We believe that American land based army aircraft may also sortie from the Letye airfields. Our radio monitors have heard reports from a Yankee army air commander who has assured the enemy carrier fleet commander that help will come from

217

other American air units, which obviously refers to land based American army aircraft. It appears that Tacloban is jammed with enemy army as well as navy planes."

Kurita pursed his lips irritably. He still had no word from Admiral Fukudome, no reconn reports from 2nd Air Fleet planes, and no word of the Kamikaze attacks on the American southern Taffy unit. Further, he had heard nothing from airmen aboard his scout planes. Kurita's only positive reports were all bad—his ships were scattered over 25 miles of open sea and these new American air attacks had been deadly with their heavier bombs.

"We have no choice but to retire; at least temporarily," Kurita said. He pointed to Cmdr. Okimuya. "You must raise 2nd Air Fleet. We must have air support to stop further American air attacks if we are to complete our mission."

"Yes, Admiral," the communications officer said.

"We have suffered severe damage and it appears we have lost two cruisers," Kurita told his staff. "Further, cruiser Kumano and destroyer Nowaki are badly damaged. We need time to make repairs and to reform battle formation; and we must be assured of air support from Admiral Fukudome's 2nd Air Fleet."

Admiral Kurita was no coward and he had no intention of calling off permanently his mission to Leyte Gulf. But he did need to assess damage and he needed to know the potential strength of the Americans. At 0930 hours, Admiral Kurita called all ship commanders. "You will retire to

218

the north at 20 knots to regroup. Destroyers Urakaze and Nowaki will remain behind to aid the sailors of our lost cruisers."

"What of the enemy carriers?" Admiral Koyanagi asked.

"We have done enough damage to them," Kurita answered. "When we reassemble we will sail to the south and steer directly for Leyte Gulf to destroy the American transports and freighter marus. We will also bombard Leyte itself, especially the airfields."

"Yes, Honorable Kurita," Admiral Koyanagi said. Then he also called the ship commanders of 1st Striking Force. "All ships will come to for 180 degrees and sail northeast at 20 knots to reassemble for new attacks."

At 0932, Admiral Ziggy Sprague, aboard the harassed CVE Fanshaw Bay, ogled in surprise. The enemy cruisers had stopped firing and were turning about to apparently retire.

"It's uncanny," Captain Carsen said to Ziggy Sprague. "What the hell's going on?"

"I don't know," Sprague answered, "but thank God for small favors."

219

Chapter Thirteen

If Admiral Clifton Ziggy Sprague expressed surprise at the withdrawal of the Japanese fleet, many of Admiral Kurita's ship commanders protested the decision. At 0935, Captain Haso Mayazumi of cruiser Tone called his commander.

"Honorable Kurita," Captain Mayazumi said, "surely, we should not withdraw. When your order came, I was already speaking to Admiral Hashimoto of Crudiv 5 and he planned to bring cruiser Haguro into column with the remaining vessels of Crudiv 7."

"I appreciate your enthusiasm, Captain," the admiral answered, "but we are too disorganized and we have been too badly harassed by enemy aircraft that now come from the American land base in Leyte. No, we must regroup. We must have intelligence on the enemy's strength, and we must have air cover from the 2nd Air Fleet. You will follow the retirement order."

"Yes, Admiral," the Tone commander answered, disappointed.

But Captain Mayazumi's complaint reflected the

220

same feeling of many other ship and division commanders in the 1st Striking Force. Next came a complaint from Admiral Susumu Kimura, commander of Desron 10. Despite the damage to his own flag, light cruiser Yahagi, and the possible loss of destroyer Nowaki, Kimura had planned to press on. He still wanted to launch another torpedo attack against the American carriers. He urgently called the fleet commander.

"Honorable Kurita," Kimura said, "we should not retire. We have destroyed at least one of the American carriers and possibly two. We have totally macerated their screen destroyers. We should press home our attack with all speed. I realize that enemy air attacks have caused considerable damage, but I do not believe such attacks are fatal. I also believe that Admiral Fukudome will soon have air cover for us."

"We are sure the Americans have jammed their fields at Leyte with aircraft that may strike again at any moment," Kurita answered his Desron 10 commander. "Until we see such air cover from the 2nd Air Fleet, we will need to keep out of range if we can."

"But we are certain our next torpedo attack will succeed," Admiral Kimura promised. "Unfortunately, the pesky American screen destroyers incited our Desron 10 sailors to launch torpedoes too soon. I have severely scolded them for this premature action and I assure you they will make no such mistake again."

"Our battle formations are in disarray," Kurita said.

"But we can reform as we continue on a southern course," Kimura said. "We could then launch torpedoes on the heels of the enemy carriers."

"I'm sorry, Admiral," Kurita said, "you will adhere to the retirement order."

"Yes, Admiral," the Desron 10 commander said.

Those aboard Yamato's bridge merely looked silently at their commander. Admiral Matome Ugaki felt depressed as he swung Yamato about and headed north. He had seen the 18" guns from his battleship wallop the American carriers, perhaps sinking two of them, and he felt sure that a continued attack would finish off the other enemy carriers. While he understood the futility of continuing the pursuit with the fleet in disarray, he saw no reason to retire.

Admiral Tomiji Koyanagi, Kurita's chief of staff, also recognized the need to reform their battle fleet, but he questioned the need to understand the strength of the enemy. He would have preferred to continue on and complete their mission, regardless of the enemy's strength. But, like Ugaki, Koyanagi said nothing.

Then came a call to Yamato's bridge from Admiral Kazutaka Shiraishi of Crudiv 7. He literally fumed at the order to retire, even though he had suffered the loss of two cruisers and serious damage to cruiser Kumano. Still, with cruiser Haguro coming up to join, Crudiv 7 would still have a powerful cruiser force. In fact, the column had almost come within 10,000 yards of the American carriers.

"Please, Honorable Kurita," Admiral Shiraishi pleaded, "I must tell you that your decision to retire is incomprehensible. I implore you to reconsider. We have utterly routed the destroyers of the American screen and they are no longer an obstacle. Further, we have seen no more enemy aircraft and perhaps they too are spent. The destruction of the American carriers is within our grasp and we must not forfeit this opportunity."

Kurita reacted calmly to Kimura's beratement. "I understand your anger, Kazutaka," Kurita told the Crudiv 7 commander. "But surely, you can see how our ships are scattered. And while I am prepared to accept losses on this mission, even heavy losses, we should not sacrifice our ships and brave sailors without hope of success. I have not given up our mission, Kazutaka, but we must give ourselves a respite. We must reorganize our columns and we must know the enemy's strength before we resume our attacks."

"I believe we should disregard the enemy's strength," Shiraishi said.

"I appreciate your courage, Kazutaka, but you must have patience. I assure you, we will continue our mission as soon as we are certain we can succeed."

"Yes, Admiral," Admiral Shiraishi answered grudgingly.

As 1st Striking Force headed north on its 280 degree bearing, the Japanese ships passed the foundering sailors from sunken USS Johnson, Hoel, and Samuel Roberts. The Japanese sailors merely stared at the U. S. bluejackets clinging to rafts or debris. The American sailors made no effort to seek rescue by the Japanese and the Japanese made no effort to save them. While the Japanese did not shoot at these sailors, the turret gunners of the 1st Striking

Force continued to send an occasional salvo of shell-fire at the rapidly disappearing American jeep carriers.

Some of the splashing American sailors from Johnson could not believe that the Japanese fleet was retiring northward. These U. S. survivors, many of whom would die before rescue, clearly believed that the big Japanese battleships could have easily finished off the jeep carriers of Taffy 3.

The withdrawal of the Japanese fleet gave damage control crews aboard the jeep carriers time to make repairs. Sailors aboard burning Kalinin Bay, no longer molested by exploding 8" and 14" Japanese salvos, worked feverishly to put out fires and to seal flooded compartments. Bluejackets aboard Fanshaw Bay also snuffed out fires and began deck repairs. Rescue operations to pick up survivors of Gambier Bay now moved smoothly, since Japanese shells no longer interfered with such rescue operations.

On Leyte, the navy air service scrub team of Tacloban also worked feverishly. Major Richard Davidson had once more stood near the runway to direct bulldozers and steamrollers that were flattening the field again, for he knew that navy planes would soon return for more service. In fact, the rollers had barely crossed the length of the airstrip when the drone of planes again emerged overhead.

"They're coming back, Sir," Lt. Worrad told Davidson.

"Okay, get your navy friend and direct them in." When Worrad nodded and moved away, Major Davidson turned to Ralph Mitchell. "General, Sir, we can use your signal flags again."

"No sweat, Major," Mitchell answered.

Soon the men at Leyte heard the TBS garble from navy pilots and crews, but this time the TBS talk reflected excited delight instead of painful despair:

"Two of the Nip cruisers are down."

"We got a destroyer; she's burning like hell."

"We got good hits on a battlewagon."

"The Goddamn Jap fleet is battered."

Meanwhile, Lt. Worrad, Army, and Lt. Forrester, Navy, again sat in their jeeps with radios to direct the landing of navy aircraft. General Mitchell, ignoring his high rank, stood on the old, narrow Japanese runway like a mere EM to flag in planes. Sgt. Sam Halpern once more alerted his ordnance crews in dispersal areas to refuel, reload, and service planes before the navy aircraft went out again. Major Davidson again readied his bulldozers and tractors to push off the strip any incoming planes that cracked up.

Then the personnel at Leyte listened in astonishment as Cmdr. Bill Keighley gave Lt. Forrester the startling report: "Lieutenant, the Japanese fleet is turning back."

"Turning back?" Forrester hissed. "Are you sure?"

"We've got at least a half dozen pilot reports," Keighley said. "They've turned tail. We'd like to hit the bastards before they get away. Can you reload and refuel us in a hurry?"

"Commander," Lt. Forrester said, "just follow our instruction, and tell your boys to keep a sharp eye for General Mitchell's signal flags. The army boys will load and refuel you and then send you on your way."

Meanwhile, Cmdr. Bob Fowler and half of the Squadron 5 aircraft returned to CVE Manila Bay to reload with torpedoes. Lt. Walt Crocker took the other flight of Squadron 5 planes to Tacloban. Crocker once more circled Leyte with his Avengers and Hellcats, waiting for Keighley's Squadron 3 to land before Ed Worrad radioed in Crocker and his airmen. Soon enough, Crocker got the word and Gen. Ralph Mitchell flagged the Squadron 3 down to safe landings. As before, some of the planes spun or skidded on the narrow runway. However, tractors quickly pulled a plane out of the way or a bulldozer simply shoved the aircraft off the strip. Then a steamroller flattened the narrow strip again.

When the Taffy 3 aircraft, more than 30 planes, alighted on the old runway and taxied to dispersal areas, the planes from the southern Taffy groups also came into Tacloban.

By 1010 hours, Sgt. Sam Halpern and his ordnance crews had begun to refuel aircraft and reload 500 pound SAP bombs, while other crews installed new .50 caliber strafing belts on the aircraft.

Lt. Walt Crocker waited impatiently as the army air force ordnance crews worked on the aircraft of Composite Squadron 3. He was anxious to get his own Composite Squadron 5 aircraft back into the air.

"Sergeant," Lt. Crocker told Halpern, "can they move faster? We don't want that enemy fleet to get away."

"Sir," the 305th Airdrome Engineer ordnance chief answered, "they're working as fast as they can. We want to knock out that goddamn Japanese fleet just as much as you do. I guarantee, I'll have all of you out of here by 1100 hours."

Lt. Walt Crocker nodded. However impatient, he would simply need to wait.

But while excited cheers from Taffy 3 sailors echoed across the decks of their jeep carriers and more cheers echoed from the army and navy men on Leyte, the Japanese were not finished. A new attack, perhaps more horrifying than the big Japanese warship guns, would soon descend on Taffy 3.

By 1045 hours, Taffy 1 of the southern escort carrier group was still trying to recover from the shock of the Kamikaze attack early this morning, and the men of Taffy 3, including Ziggy Sprague, had listened in awe to reports of the suicide pilots. Sprague could not believe that even the Japanese, who accepted death much more readily than did the Americans, would send out pilots to deliberately commit suicide, whatever the mission.

More than three hours ago, at 0735 hours, Lt. Yukio Seki had wheeled his Zero onto the head of the main runway at Mabalacat, outside of Manila. Hundreds of men had lined both sides of the field, among them Admiral Takijiro Onishi. The admiral had looked sadly at the pilots, even with regret. Still, Onishi felt a sense of satisfaction, for the news of the earlier Kamikaze attacks on the southern Taffy unit had surpassed all expectations. Returning airmen had reported four American carriers sunk by a mere half dozen suicide planes. So, Onishi fully expected these seven planes taking off now to bring similar damage to the carriers lying off Samar.

Lt. Seki had just taken off with his wingman and the next two Zeros had wheeled onto the head of the runway, when Lt. Hiroshi Nishizawa, the famed Zero pilot of the SWPA, suddenly stood next to Admiral Onishi.

"They show the ultimate in courage, Honorable Onishi," Nishizawa said.

The admiral turned and studied the lanky, pale-faced Nishizawa. "No one can deny the courage you have shown for more than three years."

"But never with the intent of committing suicide," Nishizawa answered. "I have many times expected death on a mission, but I had always known there was a chance to survive. But Lt. Seki and the others — they know they will not return."

Onishi nodded. Then, after he watched the next pair of suicide planes from the Shikishima Special Attack Force unit take off, he turned again to Nishizawa. "Is your escort ready?"

"Yes, Admiral; six aircraft. We will leave Mabalacat within the hour to join Lt. Seki's formations over the Subuyan Sea."

By 0745 hours, the six Kamikaze Zeros of the Shikishima unit had disappeared into the clouds above Manila. Then Lt. Hiroshi Nishizawa ambled to the Mabalacat operations tent for a cup of tea and a rice cake before he and his 83 Squadron pilots boarded their own planes to escort Lt. Seki and the six pilots of the Shikishima unit. When he entered the hut, he met Cap-

228

tain Rikihei Inoguchi, the 201st Air Group commander.

"Lt. Seki is airborne," Nishizawa said.

Inoguchi had nodded, but he had said nothing and Nishizawa could see that his captain felt tormented by the need to send seven pilots on a suicide mission. Inoguchi, in fact, had elected to remain here in the operations hut, for he had not mustered the courage to stand on the field and watch the Divine Wind pilots fly off. He had left the parting speech for the Kamikaze pilots to Admiral Onishi.

"You will be leaving soon?" the captain asked before he sipped more of his tea.

"Within the hour," Nishizawa said. "We will drop to low altitude on the flight over Leyte, and then to sea level over the sea to avoid the enemy's radar. The Special Attack Force aircraft will not rise to make their dives until we are nearly on top of the enemy."

"They have learned well," Captain Inoguchi said. Then he led Nishizawa to a small table and pointed to a sheet. "I have prepared a heavy strike to follow up the attack by the Shikishima Special Attack Force. Cmdr. Ishihara will take 24 Aichi dive bombers into Leyte Gulf and he will be under the escort of 20 fighter planes of the 761st Air Group under Captain Shoichi Sugita. If Lt. Seki causes enough confusion in his daring effort, the Americans will be so shocked, they will be totally unprepared to deal with conventional air attacks."

Lt. Nishizawa nodded.

"Captain Ishihara and Captain Sugita will leave at 0900 hours and they should be over target by

1100 hours. They will strike shortly after the Shikishima unit completes its mission."

"Such an effort will indeed aid the Honorable Kurita in his efforts to destroy the enemy at Leyte Gulf," Lt. Nishizawa said.

"Drink your tea and eat your cake."

"Yes, Captain."

By 1015 hours, the 13 Japanese aircraft from Mabalacat had been airborne for nearly two and a half hours. The seven Kamikaze Zeros, each loaded with a pair of 250 mg bombs, droned in a tight V and a tight diamond, while Nishizawa's escorting Zeros hung in a loose ring about the suicide planes. The escort commander squinted from the cockpit of his Zero, but he could not see clearly the faces of Lt. Seki or the others, and he could only guess how they felt at this very moment.

Nishizawa knew that Lt. Yukio Seki, an excellent pilot, had always shown a remarkable fighting spirit and fine leadership. Seki had fought hard in the Marianas, Palaus, and Yap battles. Lt. Seki had then returned to Japan for a well deserved one month leave. While home, Seki had married a long time sweetheart. Upon his return to the Philippines, Lt. Seki had been among the first to fight against the hordes of American fighter planes that had struck the Japanese air bases in the Philippines during the month of October, 1944. Then, when Admiral Onishi had asked for volunteers for the special attack corps, Lt. Yukio Seki had been among the first to volunteer. The Shikishima unit commander, only 23 years of age, was fully prepared to sacrifice his life to help the Japanese cause.

Lt. Nishizawa knew that only last night, Lt. Yukio Seki had written a farewell letter to his young, pretty bride, exhorting her to understand his decision, while he had reiterated his love for her. He had finished his letter:

"Do not mourn for me, for my greatest concern is not about death, but rather how I can be sure of sinking an enemy aircraft carrier. Think kindly of me and consider it my good fortune to have done something that is particularly praiseworthy to our Emperor."

Despite Lt. Nishizawa's own proven ability and undeniable courage, and despite his brushes with death on many occasions, the lanky lieutenant could not fully understand how Lt. Seki and the other six suicide pilots could fly to a deliberate death.

Soon, Lt. Nishizawa saw the huge land mass ahead and he picked up his inter-plane radio. "We approach Leyte, and we will begin descent. We shall fly at mountain top level and when we have crossed the island, we will drop to wave top level until I tell you to climb and to begin your dive."

"We understand, Lieutenant," Yukio Seki said.

Then the 13 Japanese pilots dropped in altitude, below the broken clouds, and droned over the hilly Leyte terrain. Nishizawa led the pilots far to the north, away from Tacloban, so he could cross the island without detection from either American visual spotters or American radar. Soon, he crossed the island, emerging over the Philippine Sea somewhere between the American jeep carriers still plying southward and 1st Striking Force now steaming northward. Nishizawa saw no ships on the surface of the sea and no aircraft around his own air formations.

"We will drop to minimum altitude," Nishizawa said. "We should reach our target in 20 minutes."

Then Nishizawa dropped his plane almost to the surface of the sea before the other planes followed. The 13 aircraft now zoomed southwest, almost skimming the water. The recently harassed Taffy 3 force was 90 miles away. The time: 1035 hours.

Aboard Fanshaw Bay, Admiral Clifton Ziggy Sprague again relaxed. Despite the loss of Gambier Bay and his three tin cans, and despite serious damage to Kalinin Bay and his own flag Fanshaw Bay, the danger from the Japanese fleet seemed to have abated. Now, as he peered from the forward window of the bridge, he saw absolutely nothing on the northern horizon. The enemy warships were out of sight. When he looked up, he saw a few planes droning overhead, apparently aircraft from Taffy 2 heading north to hit the Japanese fleet again. Sprague knew that most of his own Taffy 3 aircraft and others from the southern Taffy groups had returned to Leyte to re-arm and refuel before they conducted more air attacks against the enemy surface fleet. Some planes were re-arming with torpedoes on Manila Bay and Fanshaw Bay's own Composite Squadron 68 was already taking off again from the damaged deck of the flag ship.

Captain David Johnson watched the Squadron 68 planes take off and he then turned to Sprague. "We've got enough planes out, Ziggy, thanks to those army guys at Tacloban. Maybe they can sink a few more of those Japanese ships."

"Let's hope so," the admiral answered. "Still,

232

we'll maintain our south by southwest course to Leyte Gulf." He took a sip of coffee and then looked at Captain Carsen. "What about Kinkaid and Halsey?"

"Kinkaid's battleship-cruiser force is still barrelling north as fast as it can," Carsen answered, "and Admiral Halsey's TF 38.4 carriers expect to be in launch range about noon." Then, Captain Carsen peered to the north through binoculars. "I wouldn't worry, anymore, Admiral. The last attack pretty well did in those Japanese and these new air strikes won't do them any good. I think this thing is about over. I don't think the Japanese fleet commander wants any more."

"Relax, Ziggy, and enjoy your coffee," Captain David Johnson grinned.

"Sure," Sprague said, but he still felt somewhat uneasy.

At this same 1035 hours, on the island of Leyte, Sgt. Sam Halpern turned to Ed Huxtable of Composite Squadron 10 and grinned. "Okay, Commander, we've got your Dauntlesses and Hellcats reloaded. I'd like you to get them out of here so we can get those other Taffy units back in the air."

Cmdr. Huxtable nodded. "You did a good job, Sergeant. We're grateful."

"Just finish off that Jap fleet, Sir."

Sgt. Sam Halpern now stood by and watched the pilots of Composite Squadron 10 board their Dauntlesses and Hellcats and then lumber over the rough ground towards the airstrip. Steamrollers had again packed the strip to make the runway safe for take off. Halpern and his ordnance men

233

watched the planes roar down the runway, kicking up dirt, before they rose skyward with two 500 pound SAP bombs under their wings. Within minutes, the Squadron 10 aircraft were airborne and steamrollers quickly raced down the runway to pack the dirt again.

By 1045 hours, the first reloaded planes from the southern Taffy groups had wheeled onto the head of the runway, screaming, as pilots revved their engines and waited for a take off signal. Soon, a blinking light came from the control tower and the first two Hellcats roared down the runway. As the next pair of navy planes wheeled onto the runway and the pilots revved their engines, the whine of air raid sirens suddenly echoed across Leyte. Sgt. Halpern and the others of the 305th Airdrome Engineers did not immediately catch the air raid alert, since the siren wails had intermixed with the whine of revving Hellcat engines.

However, after the two Hellcats took off, and before the next pair of Hellcats revved engines at the head of the runway, the air raid sirens became clear. Halpern studied the sky. However, he saw nothing and he thought the air raid alert was a false alarm.

Out at sea, beyond Leyte Gulf, whoop alarms suddenly screeched throughout the decks of Taffy 3 ships as navy lookouts picked up the sight of enemy planes skimming across the water, skimming southward. Admiral Ziggy Sprague and Captain David Johnson rushed to the port side of Fanshaw Bay's bridge and looked at the planes through binoculars.

"Not much, Ziggy," Johnson said, "only about a dozen Zeros."

"What the hell do they expect to do with that?" Sprague scowled. "Call Leyte; tell any of those Hellcats still taking off to intercept the bastards. We'll only need about a dozen fighters to take care of them."

"Okay, Admiral."

However, neither Sprague, Johnson, nor anyone else in Taffy 3 was prepared for the shock in store for them. And even worse, the Americans did not know that over 40 conventional Japanese aircraft were already droning over Leyte Island to follow up with their own attack after the Kamikaze aircraft conducted their own air attack against Taffy 3's jeep carriers.

Chapter Fourteen

At 1045 hours, aboard battleship Yamato, Admiral Takeo Kurita met in the flag room with Tomiji Koyanagi, communications officer Masataki Okimuya, and Batdiv commander Matome Ugaki, along with other members of Kurita's staff. Kurita had dallied for more than an hour since his withdrawal order of 0930 hours. His disheveled fleet had reformed itself, despite the latest air strike from Taffy 2 aircraft that had caused only minor damage.

Kurita now faced his assembled subordinates. "I know that many of you disagreed with my decision to withdraw and reorganize, for in truth this delay has allowed the surviving American carriers to escape. I have searched my soul and I have concluded that you are correct. We should continue our mission, even though we have no intelligence on the enemy's true strength. We will turn southward and sail at maximum speed. I have already informed Admiral Shiraishi to order all gun crews in Crudiv 7 on battle stations and I have informed Admiral Kimura to ready all crews in Desron 10 for torpedo launch."

"A wise decision," Admiral Ugaki said.

"We will leave damaged Kumano and damaged No-waki behind, along with destroyers Ukakaze and Kiyo-shima, whose crews are on rescue operations for the survivors of cruisers Chokai and Chikuma. These two destroyers can also give a measure of protection to the damaged cruiser Kumano and destroyer Nowaki."

"Are we to forget the enemy carriers?" Admiral Koyanagi asked.

"We could not possibly catch the carriers now, before the enemy sends more air strikes and perhaps even surface ship reinforcements," Kurita said. "We will forsake the enemy carriers and sail directly into Leyte Gulf, for it is obvious now the worst threat is from the enemy airfield at Tacloban. If we destroy their aircraft they will not be able to carry out more air strikes. At the same time, we will destroy any marus we find in San Pedro Bay and we will destroy the enemy's installations at the invasion site."

Kurita's staff only listened.

"We still have formidable fire power," Kurita continued, "especially from our battleships which have suffered only minor damage."

"Yes, Honorable Kurita," Admiral Ugaki said.

Kurita turned to his chief of staff. "Tomiji, notify all ship commanders that we will turn a full 180 degrees in our reformed No. 19 battle order. Desron 10 to the starboard forward, Crudiv 7 directly forward, Desron 2 to the forward port, and our battleships in tandem, 2,000 yards to the rear and to the port rear. We will sail on a 240 degree course, south-westerly, at 26 knots."

"Yes, Admiral," Koyanagi said, "I will relay your instructions at once."

However, because of poor communications, Koyanagi would need 20 minutes before the order reached every destroyer, cruiser, and battleship commander of the 1st Striking Force. The Japanese fleet would not begin its coordinated sail until 1117 hours, and Kurita would not steer his ships into a straight path toward Leyte Gulf until 1147 hours, when he would still be 50 miles from the north entrance of Leyte Gulf. During this nearly full hour, the Japanese 2nd Air Fleet would carry out its own numbing attacks— while still keeping Kurita in the dark.

At 1047 hours, miles to the south, gunners from Taffy 3 ships opened with ack-ack fire on the Japanese Zeros zooming towards the American vessels. Antiaircraft guns from the jeep carriers and the tin cans spit 40MM pom pom and 5" bursts just above the sea at the low flying planes.

Admiral Clifton Sprague had been staring at the Japanese aircraft through binoculars. "They're coming in low. They must plan a torpedo strike. He looked at Captain Carsen. "Notify all ship commanders: evasive action against torpedo attacks."

However, before Captain James Carsen picked up the TBS the Zeros suddenly banked upwards and climbed high, their engines screaming and echoing across the sea. While ack-ack guns fired frantically from a half dozen ships, the Japanese planes simply disappeared above the broken clouds over the Philippine Sea.

"What the hell are they doing?" Clifton Sprague wondered.

"I don't know, Sir," Captain James Carsen an-

238

swered. "I was as certain as you were they'd be launching torpedoes."

When the planes disappeared into the clouds, the American antiaircraft fire ceased, and the U. S. sailors of Taffy 3 simply stared upwards or stiffened with uncertainty as the whine of aircraft engines echoed above the overcast. Like the sailors of the southern Taffy unit, these sailors of Taffy 3 could not guess that Lt. Yukio Seki was instructing fellow suicide pilots to pick out a target jeep carrier. Seki and four others would strike first, while the last two Kamikaze pilots would crash into any carrier missed by the first five pilots of the Shikishima unit. When Lt. Seki completed his instructions to the Divine Wind pilots, he called Lt. Hiroshi Nishizawa.

"We are ready, Lieutenant."

"We will come under the overcast to intercept any American fighter planes that attempt to interfere with you." Then Nishizawa paused. "Good luck to you and your pilots, Honorable Seki."

Then, at 1050 hours, October 25, 1944, the first Zero suicide pilot emerged from the clouds. Sailors of Taffy 3 watched tensely as the plane dove towards CVE Kitkun Bay in an almost perpendicular descent, the plane's engine screaming. Kitkun Bay bluejackets waited for the plane to pull out of its dive and release bombs. Instead, the plane never wavered on its aimed course towards the jeep carrier. The unwavering dive prompted Kitkun Bay gunners to fire even more furiously at the oncoming plane with 20MM, 40MM, and its 5" gun.

"Holy Christ," one of the gunners gasped, "the

239

bastard's gonna crash right on top of us; right on top of us! Just like they hit Taffy 1 this morning."

"Knock it down! Knock it down!" the gunnery chief cried.

But the sky, full of ack-ack failed to down or even alter the course of the Zero, until a 5" burst finally threw the Japanese suicide plane out of its straight dive and into a horizontal position. The plane crossed Kitkun Bay's deck from port to starboard, strafing as she crossed. Then, the Zero pilot climbed rapidly, turned, and once more dove towards the jeep carrier, this time aiming at the bridge. The Japanese pilot opened with strafing fire, but he missed the bridge, passed over the island, and crashed into the port cat-walk. The skid sheered off the plane's wing and loosened the pair of 250 mg bombs that exploded on the carrier's deck, killing five men and wounding six-teen others. The same explosion also blew apart launch line gear. The remainder of the suicide plane then bounced off the fantail of the flight deck and plopped into the sea. The Zero then sank rapidly, taking the pilot to a watery grave.

The next two suicide pilots both dove towards CVE Fanshaw Bay in an apparent mix-up in instructions. Despite the heavy barrage of ack-ack fire and the zig-zag maneuver of the ship's helmsman, the planes screamed unwaveringly towards the target. Admiral Sprague, Captain Carsen, and Captain Johnson stared in awe, like entranced frogs about to be devoured by a Gila monster. The officers' eyes widened in horror as the two Zeros came ever closer. Clifton Sprague and the others were stunned by the idea of aircraft pilots deliberately killing themselves in an effort to damage

240

or sink a ship.

Captain David Johnson finally shook himself from his stiff stance and picked up a JV. "Gunners! Gunners! You've got to knock out those planes. If they crash through the deck and explode, we'll be blown apart."

"We're doing our best, Sir," the gunnery officer answered.

The gunners maintained their desperate streams of 20MM and 40MM pom-pom fire while the jeep carrier's single 5" gun pumped shrapnel shells at the rate of a dozen a minute. Finally, several bursts of flak struck both Zeros almost simultaneously. One Zero disintegrated, its fragments dropping and splashing into the sea. The other plane bounced upwards, burst into flames, cartwheeled, and then arched into the water.

On the bridge, the rattled Clifton Sprague felt a wave of relief wash through his barrel-shaped body. Sprague fell to a sitting position on the bridge control chair, Johnson flopped into the director's chair, and Carsen fell against a bulkhead. All three men were drained.

"Goddamn, Ziggy, that was close," Captain David Johnson said.

Sprague did not answer. He only wiped the perspiration from his brow.

But the Japanese were not finished.

Now, Lt. Yukio Seki came out of the clouds, spotted CVE St. Lo, and began a dive. He ignored the spew of ack-ack fire coming up from Taffy 3 gunners, including flak from DDE's Raymond and John Butler. The bursts were so thick, the dark puffs left a polka dot of black in the low sky. From his eastern protective position under the clouds, Lt. Hiroshi Nishizawa watched Seki plunge downward, unhesitantly, with

241

obvious steady nerves that had come from three years of combat. Seki, one of the most experienced pilots among the Shikishima Special Attack Force pilots, obviously held no fear of death. In fact, the Shikishima unit commander had fully expected death long before he had volunteered for the special attack corps. Seki's concern, as he had written in his letter to his wife, was his ability to succeed against an American aircraft carrier—knock out the ship before enemy ack-ack gunners or fighter plane pilots shot him out of the sky.

As Nishizawa watched Seki dive, he suddenly heard the drone of Hellcats and he banked to see the enemy fighter planes. The American fighter pilots had been those just taking off from Tacloban, and had been diverted to intercept these Japanese planes. The Hellcat pilots were now zooming swiftly towards the Zeros, bent on shooting them down before the Kamikaze pilots could hurt the jeep carriers. Lt. Nishizawa immediately called his fellow escort pilots.

"Enemy fighter planes at nine o'clock. We must stop them from interfering with the Special Attack Force."

Then Lt. Nishizawa veered his plane and zoomed westward before the other five pilots of 83 Squadron arched their planes and followed their commander. The dogfight became short and disastrous for the Japanese. Hellcat pilots, with more experience than most of the Japanese pilots, and their planes superior to the Zero, would make short work of the Japanese pilots who were protecting the Shikishima Force suicide pilots.

As the suicide pilots of the Shikishima unit engaged in their macabre sorties, Lt. Hiroshi Nishizawa waded into the 12 American Hellcat fighter planes. In a fight that only lasted several minutes, the whine of aircraft engines, the staccato of strafing guns, and the whoosh of rockets rumbled through the low sky over Leyte Gulf. Sailors aboard ships in the gulf watched in fascination as the American pilots swiftly shot down four of the Zeros. Only Lt. Nishizawa and one other pilot escaped into the clouds to elude the U. S. Navy fighter pilots. The Americans themselves had suffered one loss, when Lt. Hiroshi Nishizawa worked his Zero behind a Hellcat and caught the plane with a burst of strafing fire and a thump from his 20MM cannon. The hits ripped off the wing of the Hellcat, shattered the cockpit, and sent both pilot and Hellcat to a watery grave in Leyte Gulf.

Nishizawa had thus chalked up his 190th victory of the Pacific war, more than any fighter pilot in the Pacific.

Despite the heavy losses to 83 Squadron, Nishizawa and his pilots held off the American interceptor pilots long enough for the Divine Wind pilots to complete their dives.

Lt. Yukio Seki, now within 100 yards of St. Lo and diving at a speed of 300 knots, had left the bluejackets aboard the jeep carrier rigid with fear. The St. Lo gunners had simply failed to knock the aircraft down or to deflect the plane from the carrier. So, suddenly, Lt. Seki smashed his plane squarely into the St. Lo flight deck. The Zero struck with such force that the aircraft penetrated the flight deck to the hangar deck below where the Zero burst into flames and then exploded its two mg bombs.

From the bridge of St. Lo, Captain McKenna, the jeep carrier skipper, had only felt a mild tremor and he thought the Japanese suicide plane had caused only slight damage. However, the initial explosion in the hangar deck set off a chain of devastating blasts. A few seconds later, small explosions sent up bursts of fire and smoke through the ripped flight deck. Captain McKenna tried to raise the hangar deck on his JV, but he got no answer. The damage, however slight, had apparently knocked out communications. McKenna turned to the bridge officer.

"Commander, go below and try to assess damage."

"Yes, Sir," the bridge officer said.

However, before the subordinate left the bridge, the St. Lo shuddered ferociously in a shattering fireball some 100 feet in diameter, as a numbing blast rocked the ship and rolled back a 200 foot length of flight deck on the aft. Then came more explosions that blew away more of the flight deck and sent twisted, heavy steel plating flying hundreds of feet into the air. The same blasts tore the entire aft elevator from its shafts, tossed the warped metal skyward, and then plopped the twisted wreckage on the macerated flight deck in heavy thuds.

The numbing explosions killed dozens of men and badly burned or seriously injured hundreds more of the St. Lo crew. Bodies of dead and wounded flew overboard to plop into the sea. Captain McKenna and his bridge staff suddenly coughed and blinked, blinded and suffocated by the thick smoke

244

and flames that now roared across St. Lo from midship to aft. And before the bridge staff reacted to this heavy damage, another series of explosions shattered the bowels of St. Lo. The fire from Seki's exploding Kamakaze plane had reached stacks of torpedoes, bombs, and gas tanks that burst in a series of booms that literally ripped the guts out of the baby flat top.

The last series of explosions blew several planes out of the hangar deck, and hurled the battered aircraft through the smashed flight deck and high into the air before fragments of planes dropped on the smashed St. Lo or plopped into the water. The same explosions had also seared both men and weapons in the gun pits, even melting some of the gun barrels before burning sailors leaped over the side and into the water. When Captain McKenna finally worked his way to the catwalk beyond the wheelhouse, wiping his eyes and coughing from smoke, he saw the entire aft enveloped in smoke and fire. Further, the ship had already listed 20 degrees to port for the explosions had also torn open the hull to start uncontrolled flooding. McKenna could only abandon ship. So, at 1100 hours, the St. Lo skipper gave the order.

"Get as many men as you can to help pass the word," McKenna told his bridge officer. "Tell them to get the wounded off first."

"Yes, Sir," the bridge officer answered.

Thus, Lt. Yukio Seki, sacrificing his life deliberately, became the first Japanese suicide pilot of World War II to sink an American ship.

At 1110 hours, survivors of St. Lo, less than half

her crew, began spilling off the ship. Even as the able lowered wounded into the water, explosions continued to shudder the ship, with one blast literally chopping away part of the hull on the starboard side. The explosion may have been a blessing, for the jeep carrier's list now went to starboard. With the huge hole, the vessel actually righted itself before listing again a full 30 degrees to starboard. By 1115 hours, the wounded were over the side, and by 1120, the able had also abandoned ship. Captain McKenna was the last man to leave, and none too soon. At 1125 hours, the St. Lo sank bow first.

The destroyer Heermann, along with DDE's Butler and Dennis steamed swiftly alongside the sinking carrier to pick up almost 600 survivors, including 300 wounded, of which 75 were litter cases.

And, while St. Lo became the first fatal victim of the newly created Special Attack Force, another of Lt. Seki's Divine Wind pilots dove after the damaged Kalinin Bay. Ack-ack fire hit the Zero and the plane soon trailed heavy smoke. But the pilot maintained his course and smashed into the port side of Kalinin Bay, chopping away deck plating and starting several fires. Luckily, repair crews had enjoyed a respite during Kurita's withdrawal to stop fires and flooding from earlier Japanese cruiser hits. Thus, damage had been under control when the suicide plane smashed into the CVE's flight deck. Repair crews quickly put out the flames and shoved the burning Zero with its dead pilot over the side and into the sea.

A moment later, the last two suicide planes,

those designated as reserves, came out of the clouds. They first also dove at Kalinin Bay. From the bridge, Captain Tom Williamson and his staff gawked in horror and watched the heavy ack-ack fire bursting in black puffs around the oncoming Zero. But, the Divine Wind pilot found his mark, smashing his plane into the port midship against this CVE that had already suffered considerable damage from Japanese surface ships. The suicide plane hit wrecked the stack and a large segment of the catwalk. The burning plane then careened in flames, arched, and splashed into the water. Fortunately, the damage was more dramatic than serious and repair crews quickly brought fires under control.

The last suicide plane from the Shikishima unit came diving towards the heretofore unscathed White Plains, one of the two remaining Taffy 3 jeep carriers that could still retrieve aircraft. Once more, anti-aircraft guns spewed heavy flak as Lucky White zig-zagged frantically to evade the diving Zero. The ack-ack gunners of White Plains finally hit the Japanese suicide plane. The aircraft burst into flames, arched out of its dive, and uncontrollably glided almost horizontally over the flight deck of White Plains. In the process, the plane exploded and threw a punishing spray of hot fragments on the flight deck. Two sailors died instantly and a dozen bluejackets suffered injury, the first casualties of the day for Lucky White.

Thus did the Zero suicide pilots of the Shikishima Special Attack Force complete their grisly mission, sinking CVE St. Lo and damaging two of the other Taffy 3 jeep carriers.

By 1135 hours, a sudden quiet settled over the Philippine Sea, except for the rescue efforts to salvage St. Lo survivors. Then, another whine of aircraft suddenly echoed from the west. Soon, 22 Judy bombers and 20 Zero fighters loomed out of the Leyte mountains to conduct a conventional air attack on the ships in Leyte Gulf and perhaps the jeep carriers of rattled Taffy 3.

By now, however, swarms of Taffy aircraft were airborne, including Hellcats from all three Taffy units. Almost immediately, Admiral Thomas Kinkaid, commander of the U. S. 7th Fleet, recalled the Hellcat units that were flying north to join the navy bombers to attack 1st Striking Force again. Kinkaid ordered the planes back to Leyte Gulf to intercept the oncoming Judys and Zeros. Captain Susumu Ishihara could not have arrived over Leyte Gulf at a less opportune time. The Hellcat fighter planes, over forty of them, pounced on the 2nd Air Fleet aircraft.

Cmdr. Ishihara frantically called Captain Shoichi Sugita.

"You must stop the enemy fighter planes," the 201st Air Group squadron leader cried.

Captain Shoichi Sugita, commander of the 761st Air Group, had been a veteran fighter pilot for more than five years, ever since he first entered combat in China. But during the past two years U. S. air power had grown and the Americans had developed superior fighter planes like the Hellcat, Corsair, P-38, and P-47. And the Japanese had lost most of their experienced pilots while increasing numbers of American pilots had gained more combat experience. Captain Sugita, with only 20 escorts, would be no match for the 40 Hellcats.

Pairs of U. S. Navy pilots waded first into the Japanese fighter planes, while pairs of other American pilots waded into the Judy bombers. Within a few minutes, the Americans shot down a dozen of Captain Sugita's 761st Air Group's fighter planes, thwarting any chance to protect the Judy bombers. Sugita could do nothing but muster his surviving Zero pilots and duck into the clouds to avoid further punishment.

Other American naval pilots knocked one after another of the Judy bombers out of the sky with heavy strafing fire and whooshing 5" rockets. Judy bombers blew up in mid air, arched down in flames, or cartwheeled into the sea. The ack-ack gunners aboard the dozens of ships in Leyte Gulf or from Tacloban itself sent up round after round of flak to knock down more of the light Japanese bombers. Within five minutes, Captain Susumu Ishihara had lost the bulk of his planes, although the Judys did manage to sink three American LST's in San Pedro Bay. But only Ishihara's own bomber and five others escaped the twin punch of Hellcat fighter planes and American antiaircraft fire.

By 1145 hours, the heavy action that had begun a half hour earlier with the Kamikaze attacks was over. CVE St. Lo was down, two more escort carriers had been further damaged, and three LST's were down. Four navy Hellcats were also down, with the loss of two pilots. On the Japanese side, all of the Kamikaze pilots, including Lt. Yukio Seki, had successfully committed suicide, and 16 other

Japanese fighter pilots, with no intention of killing themselves, were also dead. Finally, Captain Ishihara had lost most of his Judy bombers and their crews. Less than a dozen Japanese aircraft headed back to Mabalacat.

Lt. Nishizawa, Captain Sugita, and Captain Ishihara had learned a sober truth during the late morning air action. A few special attack force suicide planes had done considerably more damage than could 40 or 50 conventional aircraft. When these Japanese air leaders reported this distasteful truth on their return to Mabalacat, Admiral Shigeru Fukudome reluctantly decided to expand the Kamikaze Special Attack Corps. This late in 1944, suicide pilots apparently offered the best hope for destroying American warships.

By 1210 hours, Taffy Hellcats were zooming northward to join the Avengers and Dauntlesses already on the way to attack once more the 1st Striking Force. Cmdr. Bill Keighley led the way with his Avengers, all loaded with 500 pound SAP bombs. Behind him came Cmdr. Bob Fowler with half of his aircraft that had again loaded up with torpedoes on CVE Manila Bay. Next came Cmdr. Ed Huxtable with Composite Squadron 10 and then Lt. Walter Crocker with the remainder of Composites Squadron 5's light bombers, also reloaded at Tacloban. A few minutes behind these Taffy 3 aircraft came the southern Taffy aircraft that had also reloaded at Tacloban. Finally, Cmdr. Bob Roberts of Fanshaw Bay had reloaded and taken off again with Squadron 68 aircraft.

All of the American airmen believed the Japanese

fleet was still retiring north, presumably heading for San Bernadino Strait, and the navy airmen hoped to catch up to them before they sailed out of range. The American flyers were unaware that the Japanese fleet was now less than 80 miles from Leyte Gulf since Admiral Kurita had reversed course to the south some 45 minutes ago. The sea had calmed somewhat and the dense broken clouds had thinned.

From the bridge of Yamato, Admiral Kurita peered out at the sea through binoculars and then turned to Admiral Koyanagi. "Are we on proper course?"

"Yes, Admiral," the chief of staff answered. "We have changed from our 240 degree course to a 330 degree heading, directly towards the entrance of Leyte Gulf. At our present 26 knots, we should enter the gulf within the hour."

Kurita nodded and then peered to the south again through his binoculars. Far to the starboard forward he saw his Desron 10 under Admiral Kimura moving in a steady twin column behind flag light cruiser Yahagi. Directly ahead sailed Crudiv 7, with Desron 2, reduced to one destroyer and light cruiser Noshiro, moving in proper column. He again turned to Koyanagi.

"Is every man at battle station?"

"Yes, Honorable Kurita. Every sailor of the 1st Striking Force awaits only the word to commence fire."

Then came a call to the bridge and Koyanagi picked up the intercom. He listened irritably and then turned to Kurita. "Enemy aircraft, Admiral. Lookouts have observed 30 or 40 American light

251

bombers to the south, perhaps at a distance of four or five miles."

Kurita scowled. Then, he suddenly heard anti-aircraft fire echo from his Desron 10 destroyers to the southwest. Kurita had lost a full morning in his efforts to carry out his mission, and now he faced the possibility of losing the opportunity again. He looked dejectedly at Admiral Koyanagi.

"I fear we must again ask all ship commanders to take evasive action."

"Yes, Admiral," his chief of staff answered.

Chapter Fifteen

At 1215 hours, the 1st Striking Force was steaming south by southwest on a 330 degree course, and they had come within 75 miles of Leyte Gulf's northern entrance. Kurita had suffered air attacks on his fleet since the battle began at 0700 hours this morning. However, the attacks had been small and light until the heavy bomb attacks sometime after 0900 hours. Subsequent air attacks for the past 2½ hours from southern Taffy aircraft had also been small and relatively inconsequential.

But now, Admiral Takeo Kurita saw a horde of planes in tight formation in the distance, as many or more than he had seen all morning in a single formation. Kurita feared that land based planes from Leyte had joined U. S. Navy planes. Further, the 1st Striking Force commander strongly suspected that these oncoming American planes again carried heavy 500 pound bombs and perhaps torpedoes. Kurita pursed his lips distastefully. Where was the air support from Luzon? Uncannily, Kurita was still unaware that Kamikaze units had twice struck against American carrier forces this morning, and that a large force of conventional planes had attacked the Leyte Gulf area. Despite several efforts for the past several hours, Kurita had still failed to contact 2nd Air Fleet headquarters in Manila.

Now, as the horde of U. S. Navy aircraft came on under the broken clouds, the Japanese ships again scattered. Cmdr. Bill Keighley eyed cruiser Suzuya, the ship on which Admiral Kazutaka Shiraishi had transferred his flag after the heavy damage by USS Johnson to his Crudiv 7 flagship Kumano. The Composite Squadron 3 commander picked up his TBS and called his pilots.

"Okay, boys, we'll go after that fat cruiser. In two flights—follow me."

Despite heavy ack-ack fire from Suzuya's gunners, the American pilots peeled off and came down on the heavy cruisers. Keighley and his wingman soared towards the aft starboard and released their 500 pound bombs at 2,500 feet before arching away. Two bombs missed but the other pair of SAP's struck the main deck, aft, and tore up a chunk of deck along with a 5" secondary gun turret. The explosions killed or wounded a dozen Japanese sailors and started two fires.

Captain Watami Takahashi, the cruiser's commander, picked up his bridge phone. "Damage report! What is the damage?"

"Fires on the aft, Honorable Takahashi," the damage control officer answered. "But we are getting the flames under control."

Admiral Shiraishi, the Crudiv 7 commander, peered irritably from the same bridge at the next three oncoming bombers from Squadron 3. He relaxed momentarily when Suzuya's gunners success-fully hit one of the American Avengers, almost cutting the light bomber in half before the aircraft plopped into the sea. A second stream of ack-ack fire chopped off the left wing of the next Avenger, ignited an explosion, and forced the Avenger into a mid air roll. The plane arched over the cruiser and crossed the ship harmlessly before splashing into the sea on the port side and taking plane, pilot, gunner, and radioman to their deaths.

The third Avenger, however, sent a 500 pounder into the after stack, knocking the stack loose and igniting a huge fire.

But now came Bob Fowler with torpedo loaded Avengers from Manila Bay. Fowler and his Squadron 3 airmen launched torpedoes from 2,500 feet. Most of them missed, but a pair of torpedoes hit, punch-ing two holes in the port hull that quickly took on water in one of the engine rooms. Repair crews worked frantically to seal the flooding, but not be-for the port #2 engine went dead, slowing Suzuya's speed and bringing a list to port. Fortunately, the following aircraft of Composite Squadron 5 failed to score any more hits.

Now came Cmdr. Ed Huxtable with his five Aven-gers of Composite Squadron 10. One pair of bombs hit the quarter deck, wrecking an antiaircraft pit and destroying a wardroom. Smoke and fire sud-denly rose skyward. Before the zig-zagging Suzuya could recover from these three bomb hits, Ameri-can aircraft sent four more SAP's into the cruiser. Subsequent explosions started more fires on the quarter deck, hit the other stacks, and warped the

#2 turret gun.

Admiral Shiraishi, frantic, picked up his inter-ship radio phone and called flagship Yamato. "We must have more antiaircraft support from our destroyers. We have been seriously hit and we desperately need protection."

"We will act at once, Admiral," chief of staff Tomiji Koyanagi answered. The 1st Striking Force aide then called Desron 2 and ordered destroyers to hurry forward to the aid of damaged Suzuya.

But now, a dozen more planes went after the cruiser. Lt. Walt Crocker of Composite Squadron 5 hoped to finish off the cruiser with his six Avengers and five Hellcats. "In pairs," he radioed his pilots. "Hit the cruiser in pairs."

Despite the heavy ack-ack fire; the Japanese cruiser was too badly hit to take good evasive action and she soon took more aerial punishment. Crocker came in with his second group of Squadron 5 planes that had reloaded at Tacloban. He and his wingmen unleashed four 500 pound SAP's. Two near missed but the others ripped another pair of holes in the hull, accelerating Suzuya's list. As repair crews worked feverishly to seal increased flooding, the Squadron 5 airmen gave the battered Suzuya no respite. Although Japanese gunners knocked down two more American planes, the other aircraft of Composite Squadron 5 scored a total of ten more 500 pound hits that finished the Japanese warship.

Two hits struck the forward turret, erupting both fire and smoke. Another hit penetrated the forward deck near the bow, exploded below, and tore a hole in the prow. Two more hits struck amidship, ripping away a repair house and igniting a magazine that blew a 30 foot section of the superstructure to shreds. Huge fires then roared amidship. The final hit struck the bridge with a shattering explosion that killed every man in the wheelhouse.

Captain Watami Takahashi, his bridge officer, his communications officer, his helmsman, and two plotters died in the heavy, hot blast of shrapnel that flattened the wheelhouse. Admiral Shiraishi and his staff, in the control room behind the wheelhouse, suffered injuries, although none fatal.

With every man in the wheelhouse dead, Admiral Shiraishi himself directed operations aboard the cruiser. But he knew his ship was doomed when he got a discouraging report from the damage control officer.

"We can no longer contain flooding and fires, Honorable Shiraishi. Water pours into the starboard quarter and into the bow. Fires amidship are completely out of control and we cannot stop them. We have already suffered more than 200 men dead or wounded. I fear the ship is lost."

"There is no way to save the vessel?" Shiraishi asked.

"None, Admiral. I suggest we leave this vessel at once, before more fires ignite other magazine areas and kill many more of our sailors."

"Then we must abandon ship," the Crudiv 7 commander said.

DD's Okinami and Naganami from Desron 2, that had come up to support Suzuya with anti-aircraft fire, now found themselves on a rescue mission. The crews from the two destroyers worked quickly to bring survivors from Suzuya aboard their destroyers. Admiral Shiraishi was among them, having suffered only minor injuries. The Crudiv 7 commander ordered Tone forward so he could transfer his flag to this heavy cruiser, the second time today the admiral had been forced to change his Crudiv 7 flag.

At 1330 hours, the doomed Suzuya rolled over and sank, the third heavy cruiser victim in this battle that should have been an overwhelming Japanese victory.

Meanwhile, Cmdr. Bob Roberts with Composite Squadron 68 of Fanshaw Bay had returned to battle. Roberts took his five Avengers and five Corsairs after light cruiser Noshiro, flag of Desron 2. Cmdr. Roberts watched Noshiro zig-zag as the Squadron 68 commander approached the cruiser with his ten aircraft. The light cruiser now moved about with a single DD, Kishinami, for the division's other destroyers were rescuing Japanese sailors from doomed cruiser Suzuya. Noshiro and Kishinami's gunners sent up heavy spews of ack-ack fire, but Roberts led his planes through the heavy puffs of exploding flak.

"We'll follow the usual pattern. Attack in pairs, and stay close to your wingmen."

The Avengers and Corsairs came down on Noshiro from both sides to unleash their heavy AP bombs that crews aboard Fanshaw Bay had now found time to load. Roberts and his wingman dropped four bombs towards the forward starboard. Noshiro's helmsman successfully veered to starboard to avoid the first three bombs. One bomb, however, hit the forward area and tore a huge hole in the prow. As the other eight planes from Squadron 68 attacked Noshiro, the light cruiser danced deftly about the sea to avoid most of the bomb drops. However, the Americans scored several more hits.

One bomb struck the #2 turret forward, shattered the gunpit, and killed the gun crew. Another hit smashed the signal house and killed two men here while injuring several other Japanese sailors. Two AP's struck the stern to open holes and start flooding that soon left the stern awash and slowed the cruiser to 15 knots.

Repair crews brought fires under control and cleared damage while pharmacist mates tended wounded. But the aft was badly flooded before crews could stop the torrent of incoming sea water.

By 1225 hours, the aircraft from Taffy 3 completed their attacks. They had sunk another cruiser, damaged another cruiser and once more scattered the Japanese fleet. And, as Taffy 3 planes flew southward, 1st Striking Force got no rest.

Soon, 18 Avengers from the southern Taffy groups approached the disarrayed fleet. Among the Avengers were 12 planes that had landed at Tacloban and reloaded with 500 pound SAP's. Another half dozen Avengers had landed on CVE Savo Island of Taffy 2 and had loaded their planes with torpedoes. The 18 planes completed their runs in five minutes, losing 3 of the Avengers to antiaircraft fire, but causing more damage to Japanese vessels.

About a dozen of the planes went after the big battleships, for they had been ordered to avoid damaged vessels and to cripple other Japanese ships if they could. The American planes scored several hits, four on battleship Kongo. The strikes on Kongo knocked out a gun position, smashed storage areas, and started fires. Japanese crews aboard the battleship soon found themselves working frantically to bring fires under control and to make repairs.

But the torpedo bombers caused the most uneasiness among the 1st Striking Force sailors. Three of the six planes from Taffy 2's CVE Savo Island went after damaged heavy cruiser Kumano. Among three torpedo launches, the Avengers scored one hit on Kumano that penetrated the hull and exploded in the #1 engine room. Repair crews sealed flooding, but the engine was out and the compartment took tons of water. Now the ship had a battered prow, a heavy list, loss of one engine, and drastically reduced speed. Cruiser Kumano turned north and limped away to avoid further punishment.

The other three planes from Savo Island went after Nagato. The zig-zagging battleship sent up huge sprays of sea water even as her ack-ack gunners blackened the sky with flak. But she could not quite avoid the three skimming torpedoes, dropped within a 1,000 yards of the huge vessel. One torpedo hit the bow and punched a hole in the starboard forward. Fortunately, the hit had not struck magazines or engines and the ship did not suffer mortal damage. Still, repair crews did not stop flooding until the vessel took on considerable water and fell into a slight list. Speed dropped to under 25 knots. Nagato's commander could do nothing but turn about and streak northward in the wake of Kumano to also avoid further punishment from the serial attacks.

Admiral Takeo Kurita looked at Admiral Koyanagi who had been receiving continual reports over the inter-ship radio phone. "What are the reports of damage?" Kurita asked.

Admiral Koyanagi squeezed his face. "I fear we have lost the cruiser Suzuya. I am told that Admiral Shiraishi will transfer his flag to cruiser Tone. We also have a report of serious damage to light cruiser Noshiro and she has been forced to retire."

Admiral Kurita frowned. Then, Cmdr. Masataki Okimuya handed the admiral a report. "Our radio operators say that more enemy planes are on the way, Honorable Kurita. The American army air force is calling for aircraft to land at Tacloban. We can assume these reports refer to land based aircraft."

"And the enemy's carrier planes now have torpedoes?"

"Yes, Admiral."

"Where did they get these torpedoes? Where?" Kurita screamed.

"I do not know, Admiral," Koyanagi answered.

Even as Kurita mulled over this unpleasant news of possible more air strikes, an aide brought a message to Yamato's bridge and handed the sheet to communications officer Masataki Okimuya. The commander read the message and then gaped for a full half minute before he spoke to Admiral Kurita.

"Admiral," Okimuya said, "we have finally received a message on the fate of Admiral Nishimura's 2nd Striking Force. The communication came from the commander of destroyer Shigure."

261

"Well?" Kurita asked anxiously.

"Utter failure," Okimuya said. "In a night battle during the early hours of this morning, Admiral Nishimura suffered a most grievous defeat. The van division of 2nd Striking Force engaged an enemy battleship-cruiser force of the American support fleet. Admiral Nishimura lost both of his battleships, three destroyers, and he himself was lost. Only destroyer Shigure and the badly damaged cruiser Mogami escaped the battle."

"I see," Kurita said soberly.

"Admiral Shima in the rear division of the 2nd Striking Force also suffered considerable losses," Cmdr. Okimuya continued. "He lost a cruiser and two destroyers. He has assumed command of 2nd Striking Force and he has retired to the westward. He cannot possibly reach Leyte Gulf against this powerful American battleship force."

Not only Kurita, but also Admirals Ugaki and Koyanagi listened to Okimuya in astonishment. Only now, more than eight hours after the battle in Surigao Strait did the 1st Striking Force staff finally receive information on the whereabouts of Admiral Nishimura's 2nd Striking Force. And, before the staff of this Japanese fleet digested this horrible news, Admiral Ugaki got a call from the lookout in Yamato's crows nest.

"Enemy ships to the northeast! Battleships! Enemy battleships!"

"Are you certain?" Ugaki cried. "Are you absolutely certain?"

"Yes, Honorable Ugaki. We are certain."

The recent series of American air attacks had

rattled the Japanese sailors of 1st Striking Force, bringing on panic. So they once more allowed imagination to replace rational thinking. The lookouts on Yamato were again seeing mirages as they had called destroyers and destroyer escorts big cruisers and battleships this morning, when the Japanese fleet had unexpectedly come upon Taffy 3. At 1230 hours, no American ship lay to the northeast since 3rd U. S. Fleet was still far to the northward, chasing Admiral Ozawa's mobile fleet. Even U. S. TF 38.4 that was sailing eastward to help out Ziggy Sprague had not even come into plane launch range, much less visual range.

And Kurita's staff were also rattled from recent reports on the fate of the 2nd Striking Fleet. So they readily believed the false reports from Yamato's lookouts. Admiral Ugaki turned to Kurita.

"No doubt, these battleships are elements of the American fast carrier fleet that has come south to help the enemy carriers we have taken under attack."

Kurita nodded. "In view of these circumstances, I believe we must halt our sail to Leyte Gulf." He looked at Admiral Koyanagi. "You will order all vessels to reform into columnar position and turn northward."

"Yes, Admiral," chief of staff Tomiji Koyanagi said.

"We must conclude that we cannot successfully enter Leyte Gulf," Kurita continued. "If we continue south, we will find ourselves caught between these enemy battleships to the north and hordes of enemy carrier and land based aircraft to the south. Even if we got inside the gulf," Kurita shrugged, rationalizing, "what good would it do? The transport and freighter marus have no doubt sailed southward out of the gulf by this time and we would find no targets in San Pedro Bay."

"We were prepared to take losses," Admiral Ugaki said.

"But not for a useless effort," Kurita said. "In view of these recent enemy air attacks, we can assume that perhaps another enemy carrier force is nearby. If we sail into Leyte Gulf, we would take heavy losses for no purpose."

"What is your suggestion, Admiral?" Koyanagi asked.

"I believe we should sail north and attack this new threat, the enemy task force our Yamato scouts have just reported."

"Our fleet is still powerful, Takeo," Admiral Ugaki persisted. "Even if we do no more at Leyte than destroy the enemy airfields, such an effort will be worth any losses. Without the airfields, such an effort will be worth any losses. Without the airfields, our soldiers who fight in Leyte will have no fear of air attacks."

"No," Kurita said. "We must decide where the strength of the 1st Striking Force can do the most good. I believe the worst threat now is the enemy fast carrier fleet to the north. We should sail north and join Admiral Ozawa. Between his carrier aircraft and our battleships, we can effectively deal with the American carrier fleet [Bull Halsey's 3rd Fleet]. We will locate and attack these battleships to the northeast this afternoon. Then, we will join Admiral Ozawa to attack the other elements of the enemy's fast carrier fleet."

This time, Admiral Matome Ugaki did not answer Kurita, but he was obviously disappointed. He believed sincerely that battles could not be won, fought, or even lost without taking chances. True, they had suffered sustained aerial attacks by American planes and the determined attacks by the American tin cans, and then attacks from the unexpected land base at Leyte. Ugaki did not particularly care whether they went to Leyte Gulf or after the 3rd Fleet, but he now believed that Kurita had lost his nerve. The Batdiv commander was convinced that 1st Striking Force would do nothing more today but turn west into San Bernadino Strait and retire to Borneo.

If others besides Admiral Ugaki disagreed with Admiral Kurita, or if they expected any further battle with the enemy, no one on Yamato's bridge said anything.

Thus, at 1230 hours, with the entrance of Leyte Gulf less than an hour away, Admiral Takeo Kurita abandoned his effort. He ordered all ship commanders to sail north. Then Kurita looked at Admiral Tomiji Koyanagi.

"You will call 2nd Air Fleet again. Admiral Fukudome must send out aircraft to attack these American battleships that the Yamato lookouts have sighted northeast of our own fleet. These aircraft can attack the enemy vessels while they pinpoint the enemy's exact location for the gunners of our own 1st Striking Force. If we have a true reading on their whereabouts, we can attack with maximum results."

265

"Yes, Admiral," Koyanagi answered.

But there was little enthusiasm in Koyanagi's voice. The 1st Striking Force chief of staff, like Ugaki, did not really expect Kurita to do anything more today except to retire through San Bernadino Strait and sail westward. Koyanagi felt depressed. He was sure the battle was over and they had failed.

At 1240 hours, two Hellcat pilots from Composite Squadron 10 radioed excited news to Fanshaw Bay: the Japanese fleet was retiring to the north at flank speed.

Admiral Clifton Ziggy Sprague never altered his round face when he got the report. This latest news of a second retirement by the Japanese fleet no longer affected him. Since the first sighting of the 1st Striking Force, worry wart Ziggy Sprague had suffered through five hours of continual trauma and he was now too emotionally drained to react with any feeling.

Soon reports from other American pilots poured back to Fanshaw Bay and to the other jeep carriers and tin cans of Taffy 3. Reports also reached ships in Leyte Gulf and personnel on Leyte itself: "Japanese fleet retiring north; Japanese fleet retiring north towards San Bernadino Strait."

On Fanshaw Bay, Clifton Sprague received other good news. Kinkaid's battleships, the force that had smashed the 2nd Striking Force, had now come within visual range of the Taffy 3 lookouts. Up north, TF 38.4 expected to launch powerful air strikes within the hour against the retiring center force of the Combined Japanese Fleet. Ziggy Sprague's harrowing experience was over.

On Leyte, Major Richard Davidson, General Ralph Mitchell, Lt. Edward Worrad, Lt. Russell Forrester, Sgt. Sam Halpern, and all the others of the improvised Tacloban scrub team listened to the steady stream of good news with proud satisfaction. The scrub team had twice provided major efforts to navy planes so that Taffy aircraft had twice forced the Japanese fleet to retire.

"I guess we did our part," Lt. Worrad said.

When the drones of planes again echoed overhead, Lt. Russell Forrester sighed. "We're still not finished. We'll need to bring in those planes again."

"At least we won't have to send them out again," Worrad grinned.

At 6th U. S. Army headquarters in Tacloban, both General MacArthur and General Krueger sighed with relief at the news of the Japanese fleet retirement. Still, MacArthur had lost none of his bitterness for Admiral William Bull Halsey. He would continue his feud with the U. S. fleet commander until the end of the war.

And, as suspected by many of the 1st Striking Force staff, Admiral Takeo Kurita did not engage anybody else on October 25, 1944. Instead, he indeed turned west through San Bernadino Strait at nightfall to sail back to Brunei in Borneo. 3rd U. S. Fleet planes hit the 1st Striking Force during the morning of October 26. But, except for sinking the cripples, destroyer Nowaki and light cruiser Noshiro, they did little other damage. Kurita successfully reached Borneo with the rest of his center force fleet. He thus gained a respite to fight another day.

Admiral Soemu Toyoda, Commander-in-Chief of the Japanese Combined Fleet, soon realized the utter failure of his Sho-I plan gamble. He knew his navy would not disrupt the American reconquest of the Philippines. General Hisaichi Terauchi, commander of the Japanese 35th Army, knew that the failure of the Japanese fleet meant he would not drive the American invaders from Leyte Island. In Manila, General Tomoyuki Yamashita, the Tiger of Malay, expected the Japanese fleet debacle to affect him. He guessed that the Americans would sooner or later come to Luzon and he would lose the Philippines.

At Mabalacat, both Admiral Shigeru Fukudome and Admiral Takijiro Onishi interpreted Kurita's failure as an extension of their own failure to stop the Americans with their 2nd Air Fleet. These Japanese air commanders expected land based planes from the U. S. Army 5th Air Force to soon arrive in Leyte. These land based planes would further decimate 2nd Air Fleet as the American 5th Air Force had decimated Japanese air units in New Guinea, the Solomons, New Britain, and the East Indies. The only glimmer of hope was the new Kamikaze Special Attack Corps that had proven so successful in their attacks on the American jeep carriers of Taffys 1 and 3.

Admiral Takijiro Onishi would find ample volunteers for his Kamikaze Corps.

In the end, however, Onishi would subject himself to a most horrible death. On the day of Japan's surrender, August 15, 1945, Onishi went to his study and jabbed a sword through his abdomen in an act of hari-kari suicide. However, he had refused all aid to accelerate his death. Instead, he had elected to endure bleeding, agonizing pain for twelve hours before he finally died. Onishi had no doubt indulged in this extended self suffering to atone for his inward guilt from sending hundreds of young men to their deliberate death in the Kamikaze Special Attack Corps.

For Admiral Clifton Ziggy Sprague, October 25, 1944, had been one of courageous determination, magnificent effort, and unselfish valor against the worst kind of odds for himself and the sailors and airmen under his command. Taffy 3 units would receive both Presidential and Unit citations for their remarkable gallantry. Both U. S. sailors in San Pedro Bay and U. S. soldiers on Leyte owed their survival to the sailors and airmen of Taffy 3, with an assist from the Tacloban scrub team who serviced navy planes with army facilities.

October 25 marks the date of the Feast of St. Crispins, a day on which a small force of English bowmen defeated a powerful French army on the fields of Agincourt during medieval times. In his play *Henry V,* William Shakespeare said of this remarkable victory:

"And Gentlemen in England now abed
    Should think themselves accursed they were
        not here,
And so hold their manhoods cheap,
    Because they fought not with us on St.
        Crispin's Day."

In the years that passed since that 25th day of October in 1944, military historians have paid the same tribute to Clifton Ziggy Sprague and his sailors and airmen. They praised the courage of these Taffy 3 bluejackets and aviators for their remarkable victory, as Shakespeare had praised the English bowmen who won that notable battle on St. Crispin's Day some 500 years earlier.

Bibliography

BOOKS

Blair, Clay, Jr., *Silent Victory,* J. P. Lippincott & Co., Philadelphia, 1955

Boggs, Major Charles W., *Marine Aviation in the Philippines,* Historical Division, U. S. Marine Corps, Washington, DC, 1951

Craven, Wesley, & Cate, James, *The Pacific: Matterhorn to Nagasaki,* Vol. 5, The Army Air Forces in WW II, U. of Chicago Press, 1953

Creswell, John, *Sea Warfare, 1939-1945,* Univ. of Calif. Press, Berkley, Calif., 1967

Dull, Paul S., *A Battle History of the Imperial Japanese Navy,* Naval Institute Press, Annapolis, Md., 1978

Falk, Stanley L., *Decision at Leyte,* W. W. Norton Co., New York City, 1966

Field, James R., *The Japanese at Leyte Gulf,* Princeton Univ. Press, Princeton, N.J., 1947

Hess, William N., *Pacific Sweep,* Zebra Books, New York City, 1978

Hoyt, Edwin P., *The Battle of Leyte Gulf,* Waybright and Talley Publishers, New York City, 1972

Ito, Masanori, with Pineau, Roger, *The End of the Japanese Navy,* W. W. Norton and Co., New York City, 1956

Koyanagi, Tomiji, *The Kurita Fleet,* Ushio Shobo Pub., Tokyo, 1956

Matome, Ugaki, *Record of Sea Battles,* Nippon Shuppan Kyodo Pub., Tokyo, 1956

Millot, Bernard, *Divine Thunder* (Japanese accounts translated by Robert Laffant), McCall Publishing Co., New York City, 1972

Morison, Samuel, *Leyte, Vol. XII,* from *History of U. S. Naval Operations In WW II,* Little, Brown, & Co., Boston, 1963

Potter, John Deane, *The Life and Death of a Japanese General,* Frederick Muller Ltd. Publishers, London, Eng., 1962

Roscoe, Theodore, *United States Destroyer Operations in WW II,* U. S. Naval Institute Press, Annapolis, Md., 1953

Shores, Christopher, *Fighter Aces,* Hamlyn Publishers, London, Eng., 1975

Toland, John, *The Rising Sun,* Random House, New York City, 1970

Toliver, Raymond, & Constable, Trevor, *Fighter Aces of the U. S. A.,* Aero Publishers, Fallbrook, Calif., 1979

Woodward, C. Van, *The Battle for Leyte Gulf,* Macmillan & Co., New York City, 1947

PERSONAL ACCOUNTS

Fukudome, Shigeru, "The Battle off Formosa," *Proceedings,* May, 1952, U. S. Naval Institute,

Annapolis, Maryland.

Hagen, Robert C., Lt., "We Asked for the Jap Fleet and Got It," *Saturday Evening Post*, Vol. 217, May 27, 1945

Hathaway, Amos, Cmdr., "The Battle As I Saw It," *American Magazine*, Vol. 139, April, 1945

Hubbard, Lucien, "Scrub Team at Tacloban," *Readers Digest*, Feb., 1945

Inoguchi, Rikihei, "The Kamikaze Creed," *Proceedings*, Feb., 1973, U. S. Naval Institute, Annapolis, Md.

Koyanagi, Tomiji, "The Battle of Leyte Gulf," *Proceedings*, May, 1952, U. S. Naval Institute

Nakajima, Tadashi, & Inoguchi, Rikihei, "The Kamikaze Attack Corps," *Proceedings*, June, 1960, U. S. Naval Institute, Annapolis, Md.

Sprague, Clifton, Admiral, "The Japs Had Us On the Ropes," *American Magazine,* Vol. 139, April, 1945

RECORD SOURCES

Archive Records, Naval Historical Center, Washington, DC

Microfilm File #1979-4, Taffy 3 Action Reports in Samar, Action of Battle for Leyte Gulf
    Task Unit 77.4.3, Admiral C. A. F. Sprague
    Task Unit 77.4.32, Admiral R. A. Ofstie
    Fanshaw Bay, CVE 70 (flagship)
    Kalinin Bay, CVE 371
    Kitkun Bay, CVE 68
    St. Lo, CVE 63
    White Plains, CVE 66

Gambier Bay, CVE 73
Heermann, DD 532 (flagship Desron 46)
Hoel, DD 533
Johnson, DD 557
Raymond, DDE 341
Dennis, DDE 405
Samuel B. Roberts, DDE 413
John C. Butler, DDE 339

Naval Air Action Reports, Carrier Air Group #26
  Microserial #92233, Composite Squadron 3,
    Oct. 18-26, 1944
  Microserial #93720, Composite Squadron 5,
    Oct. 25, 1944
  Microserial #95530, Composite Squadron 10,
    Oct. 25, 1944
  Microserial #139253, Composite Squadron 68,
    Oct. 25-28, 1944
Motor Torpedo Boats Report
  Microserial #FC 8 7-A16-3, MTB Squadron 7,
    Oct. 21-24, 1944

JAPANESE RECORDS ON MICROFILMS (action reports)

Sho Operation
  JD 2 Operation Records Doc. #WDC 1610056,
    NA 12604
      1st Striking Force - Oct. 16-28, 1944
      BB Hurana - Oct. 24-26, 1944
      BB Kongo - Oct. 22-28, 1944
      BB Yamato - Oct. 17-28, 1944

Document #161005, NA 11744
    Crudiv 7 - Oct. 23-26, 1944
    Desron 10 - Oct. 17-27, 1944
JD 3 Operations Records #161638
    Batdiv 1 War Diary, Oct. 1-31, 1944
    Desron 2 War Diary, Oct. 1-31, 1944
    Desron 10 War Diary, Oct. 1-31, 1944
    Crudiv 5 War Diary, Oct. 1-31, 1944
    Crudiv 7 War Diary, Oct. 1-31, 1944

PHOTOGRAPHS AND CHARTS

All photographs from National Archives, Still
    Picture Section, Washington, DC
All maps and charts from Naval Historical Center,
    Washington, DC

Participants

Japanese

Japanese Combined Fleet — Admiral Soemu Toyoda
  1st Striking Force (center force)
    Admiral Takeo Kurita — commander
    Admiral Tomiji Koyanagi — chief of staff
    Cmdr. Masataki Okimuya — communications officer
  Batdiv 1
    Yamato — Admiral Matome Ugaki
    Nagato — Admiral Yusi Kobe
  Batdiv 3
    Kongo — Admiral Tosi Shimazaki
    Haruna — Admiral Kuse Shigenaga
  Crudiv 7 — Admiral Kazutaka Shiraishi — commander
    Kumano — Captain Sasi Hitomo
    Suzuya — Captain Watami Takahashi
    Chikuma — Captain Suzuki Norimitsu
    Tone — Captain Haso Mayazumi
  Crudiv 5 — Admiral Shintaro Hashimoto — commander
    Haguro — Captain Kato Sugiura
    Chokai — Captain Keno Ariga

Desron 10—Admiral Susumu Kimura—commander
   Yahagi (light cruiser)
      Captain Masi Yoshimura—captain
      Cmdr. Tadasi Otani—gunnery officer
   Destroyers:
   Nowaki—Captain Tone Tanii
   also: *Urakaze, Kiyoshima, Isokaze, Fujinami,
      Hamakaze, Yukakaze*
Desron 2—Admiral Mikio Hayakawa—commander
   Noshiro (light cruiser) Captain S. Kajiwara
   Destroyers:
   Kishinami, Naganami, Okinami

2nd Striking Force—(southern force)—Admiral
   Shoji Nishimura
      Forward section—Admiral Shoji Nishimura
      Rear section—Admiral Kiyohide Shima

Mobile Force (northern force) Admiral Jisaburo
   Ozawa

2nd Air Fleet, Manila, Luzon—Admiral Shigeru
Fukudome, Commander
   6th Base Air Force, Clark Field, Luzon—Admiral Takijiro Onishi
      201st Air Group—Captain Rikihei Inoguchi
         83 Squadron—Lt. Hiroshi Nishizawa
         Shikishima Special Attack Force—Lt. Yu-
         kio Seki
         Yamato Special Attack Force—Lt. Yo-
         sunori Aoki
      761st Air Group—Captain Shoichi Sugita
      701st Air Group—Captain Susumu Ishihara

Americans

Allied Forces, SWPA—General Douglas MacArthur—
Commander in Chief
    U. S. Sixth Army—General Walter Krueger
        305th Airdrome Engineers Battalion
           Major Richard Davidson—Commander
           Captain Bradford Whitemore—Deputy
              Commander
           Lt. Edward Worrad—Construction Chief
           Sgt. Sam Halpern—Ordnance Chief
        1st Marine Air Wing (advanced echelon)
           General Ralph Mitchell—Commander
           Lt. Russell Forrester—Navy Liaison Officer

3rd Fast Carrier Fleet—Admiral William Halsey

7th Support Fleet—Admiral Thomas Kinkaid
    Taffy 3 Escort Group—(Carrier Air Group 26)
    Admiral Clifton Sprague
        CVE Fanshaw Bay—Captain David Johnson
           Composite Squadron 68—Cmdr. Bob
           Roberts
        CVE Kalinin Bay—Captain Thomas Wil-
        liamson
           Composite Squadron 3, Cmdr. William
           Keighley
        CVE Gambier Bay—Captain William Viewig
           Composite Squadron 10—Cmdr. Edward
           Huxtable
        CVE Kitkun Bay—Captain James Whitney
           Composite Squadron 5—Cmdr. Robert
           Fowler

CVE St. Lo – Captain McKenna
  Composite Squadron 65 – Lt. Cmdr. Ron
  Jones
CVE White Plains – Captain David Sullivan
  Composite Squadron 4 – Lt. Edward Fick-
  enscher
Desron 46 (screen for Taffy 3) Captain William
Thomas
  Destroyers:
  USS Hoel – Cmdr. Larry Kintberger
  USS Johnson – Cmdr. Ernest Evans
  USS Heermann – Cmdr. Amos Hathaway
  Destroyer escorts:
  USS Dennis – Lt. Cmdr. Sam Hensen
  USS John Butler – Lt. Cmdr. Joe Pace
  USS Raymond – Lt. Cmdr. Al Byer
  USS Samuel Roberts – Lt. Cmdr. Robert
  Copeland

Southern Taffy forces – Admiral William Sam-
ple, deputy commander
  Taffy 1
  *CVE's Sangamon, Suwannee, Chenango,
  Santee, Saginaw Bay, Petrof Bay*
  DD's Trathen, Hazelwood
  DDE's Edmonds, Bull, Eversole, Coolbaugh
  Taffy 2
  CVE's Manila Bay, Marcus Island, Savo Island

Battle off Samar, 25 October 1944

IJN Destroyer track
IJN Cruiser track
IJN Battleship track
USN Escort Carrier Unit "Taffy 3"

Haruna
Kongo
Chikuma
Suzuya, Yahagi and DD's
Nagato
Chokai
Kumano
Yamato
Tone
Noshiro and DD's

Suzuya

Hoel

Gambier Bay
Johnston
Roberts

Chikuma
Chokai
Kumano

25 OCTOBER 1944

NAUTICAL MILES
5   10   15
5000 11000 19000 25000 37000
YARDS

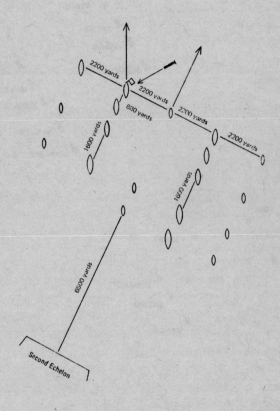

Formation of First Echelon of Northern Force at the time the heavy cruiser Atago was torpedoed by the Darter.

First Diversion Attack Force, Vice Admiral Kurita, cruising disposition at time of submarine attack, October 23. Note the remarkable and costly failure to station destroyers ahead of the heavy ships while passing through known submarine waters.

The BATTLE for LEYTE

Wright

BILIRAN

SAMAR

N

CARIGARA BAY

La Paz

n Isidro

Carigara

Limon

BREAKNECK
RIDGE

Tacloban

MT.
CANGUIPOT

HIGHWAY 2

Jaro

"DEATH
VALLEY"

Palo

Tanauan

HIGHWAY 2

Dagami

Palompon

Ormoc

Burauen

Dulag

MARABA G R.

ORMOC
BAY

LEYTE GULF

AMOTES

Abuyog

SEA

Baybay

Miles   20   palacies

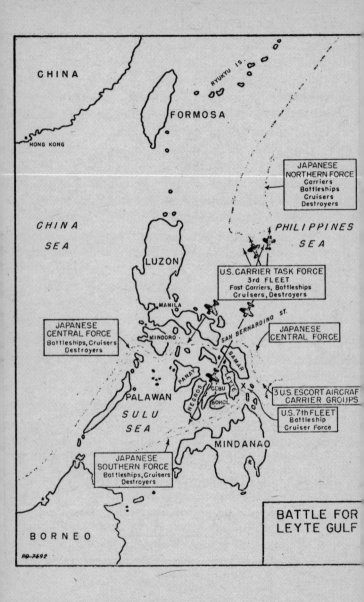

CHINA

RYUKYU IS.

FORMOSA

HONG KONG

CHINA SEA

PHILIPPINES SEA

JAPANESE
NORTHERN FORCE
Carriers
Battleships
Cruisers
Destroyers

LUZON

U.S. CARRIER TASK FORCE
3rd FLEET
Fast Carriers, Battleships
Cruisers, Destroyers

MANILA

JAPANESE
CENTRAL FORCE
Battleships, Cruisers
Destroyers

SAN BERNARDINO ST.

JAPANESE
CENTRAL FORCE

MINDORO

SAMAR

PANAY

LEYTE

NEGROS

CEBU

3 U.S. ESCORT AIRCRAFT
CARRIER GROUPS

PALAWAN

BOHOL

U.S. 7th FLEET
Battleship
Cruiser Force

SULU
SEA

MINDANAO

JAPANESE
SOUTHERN FORCE
Battleships, Cruisers
Destroyers

BORNEO

BATTLE FOR
LEYTE GULF

RD 7692

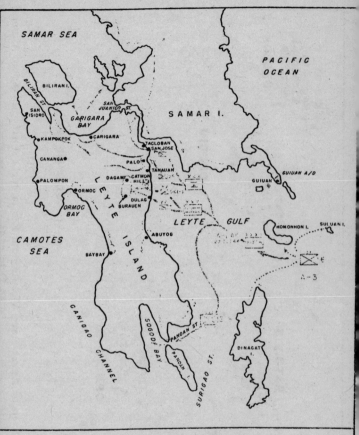

PLAN FOR THE
LEYTE-SAMAR OPERATION
THE THREE PHASES

Phase One   Phase Two   Phase Three

10   0   10   20   30 MILES

Okinami
Naganami
Kishinami
Noshiro
DESRON 2

CRUDIV 7

Suzuyo
Tone
Chikuma
Kumano

Kongo
Haruna

BATDIV 3

Nagato
Yamato

BATDIV 1

Chokai
Haguro

CRUDIV 5

Yukikaze   Nowaki
Hamakaze   Kiyochima
Fujinami   Urakaze
Isokaze   Yahagi

DESRON 10

|— 1000 METERS

First Diversion Attack Force, Vice Admiral Kurita, night search disposition. Assumed 0155, October 25.

Admiral William Bull Halsey — commander American 7th Fleet.

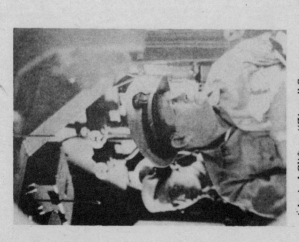

Admiral Clifton ''Ziggy'' Sprague — commander of Taffy 3.

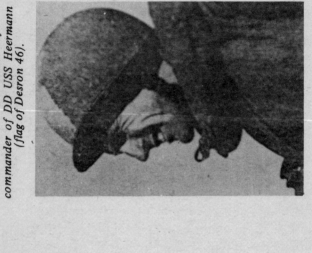

Cmdr. Amos Hathaway —
commander of DD USS Heermann
(flag of Desron 46).

Cmdr. Ernest "Cherokee" Evans —
Johnson. commander of DD USS

Captain David Johnson – skipper of CVE Fanshaw Bay.

*General Ralph Mitchell —
Commander 1st Marine Air Wing, Leyte.*

Admiral Soeumu Toyoda, the last commander
in chief of the Combined Fleet.

Admiral Soeumu Toyoda –
commander of Japanese Combined Fleet.

Sgt. Sam Halpern, ordnance chief
of 305th Airdrome Engineer Battalion.

Admiral Takeo Kurita —
commander of 1st Striking Force.

Admiral Matome Ugaki —
commander of Batdiv, 1st Striking Force.

Admiral Susumu Kimura—commander of Desron 10, 1st Striking Force.

Admiral Kazutaka Shiraishi—
commander of Crudiv 7, 1st Striking Force.

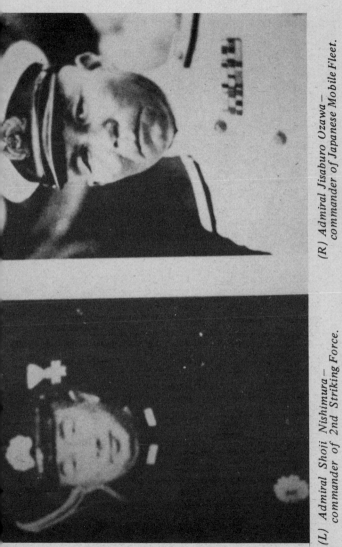

(L) *Admiral Shoji Nishimura—commander of 2nd Striking Force.*

(R) *Admiral Jisaburo Ozawa—commander of Japanese Mobile Fleet.*

Gen. Sosuki Zuzuki — commander 35th Japanese Army, Ley

Admiral Takijiro Onishi —
commander of Japanese 6th Base Air Force.

Captain Rikihei Inoguchi—
commander 201st Japanese Air Group.

Lt. Hiroshi Nishizawa — leader of Japanese 83 Squadron.

*Captain Shoichi Sugita —
commander of Japanese 761st Air Group.*

Lt. Yosunori Aoki — leader of Yamato Special Attack Force.

General Douglas MacArthur returns to Philippines, one day after invasion.

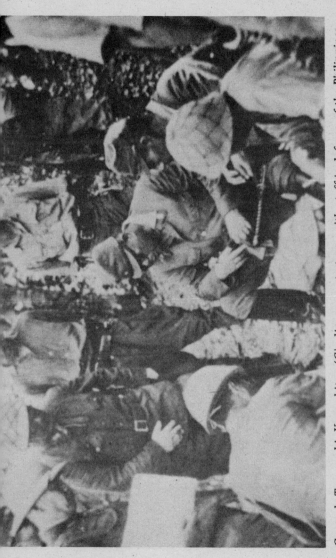

General Tomoyuki Yamashita—(C) discusses strategy with staff in defense of the Philippines.

These pilots from carrier USS Lexington sank BB Musashi, but brought back exaggerated reports that almost caused disaster at Leyte.

Japanese air crews of 201st Air Group prepare to make air strikes on Leyte Gulf.

Crew of DD USS Johnson at commissioning ceremonies in Seattle, Wash.

Gen. Onishi, far left, exhorts his Kamikaze pilots at Mabalacat..

DD USS Heermann starts making smoke during battle of Samar.

U. S. Taffy 3 escort carrier group comes under attack.

Destroyers of U. S. Desron 46 lays smoke screen in Battle off Samar.

CVE Gambier Bay badly hit and burning during battle of Samar.

CVE Kalinin Bay burning from hits by Japanese cruisers.

DDE's of Taffy 3 make smoke to hide burning CVE Kalin Bay in battle of Samar.

Gambier Bay burns fiercely before going down.

A long range view of U. S. escort carrier CVE Gambier Bay as she burns.

Tacloban airfield, new runway at left, old Japanese airstrip at right.

These navy planes await reload and refuel at Tacloban before going off again to hit Japanese fleet.

Reloaded Navy Hellcat takes off from Army Air Force airfield in Tacloban. Army Air Force personnel in bomb hoist truck (L) serviced the navy planes.

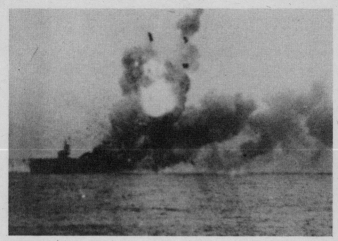

U. S. CVE St. Lo erupts in tremendous explosion after hit by Japanese suicide pilot, Lt. Yukio Seki.

Crew of CVE Kalinin Bay bury their dead at sea after battle.

Battleship Kingo of the 1st Striking Force.

Battleship Yamato makes steam.

BB Musashi fatally hit by American carrier planes.

BB Kongo under air attack by U. S. carrier planes.

BB Musashi and cruiser Mogami under attack by U. S. carrier planes.

Cruiser Chikuma erupts in fatal fires and smoke after air attack.

Cruiser Suzuya and Japanese destroyer, background, under attack by U. S. Navy planes from loaded at Tacloban.